THE JOB HUNTER

The Diary
of a "Lost" Year

THE
JOB
HUNTER

The Diary of
a "Lost" Year

ALLEN R. DODD, Jr.

McGraw-Hill Book Company

New York   London   Toronto

CONTENTS

Contents

INTRODUCTION

This book was developed from an article which appeared under the same title in the November 30, 1962, issue of *Printers' Ink* magazine.

For some months after the article appeared readers of *Printers' Ink* wrote or telephoned to ask a number of questions:

Was the Job Hunter an actual person? The answer was no. He was a composite figure, a typical white-collar job-seeker, created from a variety of sources. His story was told in fictionalized, first-person style because this seemed the most effective way in which to present the unemployed white-collar man's personal plight and its impact on his family and his community. He had to have some profession, of course, and *Printers' Ink* is an advertising magazine, so he became an advertising man. The Job Hunter of the article and of this book, therefore, is not the author, nor is he any other single individual. While the "hidden depression" is only too real, the characters, organizations and incidents in this book are fictitious and any resemblance to actual people, living or dead, or organizations is purely accidental.

Do such job hunters ever return to positions similar to the ones they lost? The answer, obviously, is both yes and no. Some unemployed white collar people do; it is the author's belief that a large number do not. They return to the employment rolls and, in many cases, to responsible positions but many still remain "displaced persons." A return to affluence is possible but never a return to innocence, and many men who have been brought face-to-face with harsh realities are no longer attracted by the old incentives.

How extensive is such unemployment? The author does not pretend to know. Some jobless white collar people, through pride or a conviction that a job is just around the corner, do not apply for compensation. Others are forced by financial pressures into jobs far below their capacities; they are technically "employed" though the community is not using their skills and their position in life has been drastically downgraded. It should be unnecessary to add that the unemployed executive may differ from the unemployed factory worker only in the length of time it takes his savings to run out. Once they do run out, he faces exactly the same problems. This is the story of one man's encounter with those problems, an encounter which became a long journey into reality. Reality is many things: it is fear and it is hope, it is insecurity rather than the illusion of security, it is the bite of bitterness and the warmth of joy, it is being alive. The Job Hunter lost much and gained much through his journey and the reader will have to add up the score as he sees it and write his own moral. He will find no other one in these pages.

There is no dedication on the title page of this book because it owes its existence to many people. These include Woodrow Wirsig, former editor of *Printers' Ink,* who published the original article and forcefully encouraged the production of the book, Ivy Dodd, my wife, who supplied efficient aid and endless encouragement, and, of course, the job hunters whose problems inspired this work. Beyond any particular individuals, this book is directed to all those bewildered men and women who find themselves exiles from their own society, with the author's confidence that they will, by whatever roads and through whatever trials, find their way home.

The Man
on the Bench

One afternoon I sat in the park.

It was a New York winter's day, cold and sunny and so clear that I could have seen from one end of Manhattan to the other if I had been up in an executive suite instead of down in the park. I sat down on a bench and thought about myself and my life and I felt a little sick, because I realized that nothing would ever be the same again.

It was a Wednesday afternoon, one of those noisy, churning, midweek afternoons in Manhattan, and I was sitting in the park because it was only three o'clock and I was forty-five years old and, for the first time in my life, I had no place to go.

A few months ago it had been call Joe Marks, Miss Halley, and tell him I'm sorry as hell but I can't make it for lunch today and then buzz Harry and remind him to have that stuff ready by two sharp because I have to be downtown by three and oh, hello, Sid; I'd like to talk it over but I'm up to my eyebrows so let me call you back. Then something happened and I was out. I was still up to my eyebrows, however, because I was between positions, I was looking over the field, I was hashing it over with Joe and Sid and the boys downtown and it was all going to be firmed up in a few days, but somehow it never was. The meetings dwindled away, the gaps between them became broader and I had to work harder and reach out further to fill each day with appointments. That Wednesday the clock ran down. There weren't any phone calls left to make or any letters left to write or any people left to see. I wasn't "between positions," I was unemployed and apparently unemployable. I was just one more domestic displaced person; a jobless white-collar worker.

I sat in the park until train time with two questions turning in my mind: where do I go tomorrow, and how the hell did all this happen to me?

"It's Going to Be Tough on the Company, of Course"

When I look back at the whole business over the gulf of the past year I can see a lot of things which I mishandled. In July, the last month of the old life, I would have called myself a shrewd businessman, and perhaps I was. I was also totally unprepared for what I was about to face; when I stepped out of that office I didn't know what I was stepping into. There were opportunities and I missed them, there was money and I wasted it, there was time and I fumbled the days away.

I should have grasped what was happening to me, but I didn't; a man falling down a flight of stairs doesn't count the steps. I had very little job-hunting experience and I didn't know that job-hunting is a fine art. Ironically, it's the professionals—the job-hoppers and the hard-luck lads—who are best at the game. They are specialists in survival; they can sense which offers are likely to pay off and which ones will merely waste valuable time. Their families are experts in the esoteric business of budgeting without income; they've learned that it costs money to be unemployed. It's the long-settled men, fifteen to twenty years in one job, who throw away their savings and invest their hours badly.

It's the long-settled men, too, who are out of touch with their times. The pro is up to the minute; he knows that gray temples and experience are out this year, crewcuts and callowness are in. He knows where business is slow though the drums of prosperity may be going boom, boom, boom; he knows that affluence can be a cardboard castle and that the best jobs are not found with the firms which have money, but with the firms which have problems.

Finally, I believe, I underestimated the emotional pressure of unemployment. I saw something of psychological shock during the war and it can do funny things to a man. He may feel normal, he may act assured; but the injury is there and it shows itself in lassitude, disorganization, depression and quick-flaring fear. I was jaunty during those first few weeks; "there's no problem," I said and I believed it. But something had been broken inside and it may never be whole again.

I suppose you could call me a second-generation suburbanite. I was born in Cleveland and when I was about twelve the insurance firm my father worked for transferred him to New York. We bought a small house in Connecticut. It was a tough proposition for the old man to swing but he had a tiny bit of capital and in the early 1930s that was everything. There's a legend now that nobody saw the crash coming, but that isn't so. A lot of people saw it coming but there wasn't much they could do about it. Like it or not, they were being dragged along on the big balloon ride and all they could do was hang on to whatever they had and hope.

My father held on to his job and that was everything, too. A lot of kids today have never seen anything but salary increases, but men used to come home and say, "Well, I got another pay cut." The first thing a wife always asked was "You're going to keep your job, aren't you?" and it was only after her husband said yes that she started figuring out how to get by on less. That was the big thing, to be employed and not just one more person that nobody needed.

The other day one of our neighbors remarked that two cars were really essential in the suburbs and I remembered that we didn't even own a car until 1935. My father walked to the station and my mother took the bus to the stores. Some days she made two trips. Saturday was the big shopping day and on Saturdays my older brother Clifford and I went along to "help carry." The late 1930s rolled by; I was a teen-ager, but being a teen-ager in those days was merely a transition and not a profession. Then the war came crunching down, and when things started up afterwards they didn't start up from the same point. Cliff went into the Air Force and was killed in 1943. I was going to apply for Officer Candidate School, but I put in for overseas service in tanks instead because of Cliff and I stayed an enlisted man. People did that sort of thing during the war. My father died in 1944—I don't think he ever got over Cliff's going that way—and my mother went to live with her sister in Cleveland.

A couple of months before I got out of the Army, Mr. Glenfield, my father's old boss, wrote me a letter asking me to drop in when I got back to New York, and I did. Sometimes I wonder where I would be and what I would be like if I had taken the job he offered. I'd be married to somebody else and the kids wouldn't be the same kids. It scares you, sometimes, when you look back and see how much can hang on a simple "yes" or "no." At the time I was merely four years behind and in a hurry to catch up. The advertising business seemed to be a place where things happened fast and when a junior copywriting job popped up I grabbed it. Besides, the salary was terrific: sixty dollars a week.

Janet grew up in Illinois and went to dramatic school there and came to New York after the war. She landed a job with one of the big networks and I met her when I went over to the studios one day to straighten out some mix-up in a commercial. We were married a few months later.

I can skim over the rest of my career in a few sentences and that in itself may be one clue to the way it all ended. We just put our heads down and started running and if you had asked us where we were heading we would have said, "Why, up; of course." I changed agencies twice in six years, moving up each time, and when my thirty-eighth birthday arrived I was a senior executive and pretty much of a specialist in some types of accounts. I had found my niche in the glass cliffs of Manhattan.

It was not only possible but necessary to move back to Connecticut. The old house was gone, but it wouldn't have suited us anyway. The best residential district was on the other side of town now and we found a fine, modern split-level with plenty of yard space for young Cliff and little Skip.

Mother was delighted. "It's nice to know that you're finally 'back home,' " she wrote—she had always had a habit of putting

|5|

quotes around cliches—"and I'm sure all our old friends will be delighted to see you." I did make a conscientious effort to look up old acquaintances, but the only person who bridged the years and became a part of our new circle was Max Weltchek, who used to run the hardware store and now owned a large plumbing and marine supply business. Max was a funny guy in a lot of ways, apart from the fact that he didn't commute. He was the mentor of amateur yachtsmen and the terror of cocktail parties; a wry, candid character who could slash a conversation apart with one sharp-edged remark. Some people didn't like him, others called him "quaint," but nobody ever quite figured him out. Something about Max always suggested that he was holding words back, even at his most talkative.

We bought a second car, a small British model, and we junked all our old furniture and launched our new home with new possessions. These things were incidental, of course; what really mattered was that we were in the right place, right for ourselves and right for the children. There were good schools and the better sort of kids for them to mix with, and that was important. These days you have to start thinking about college early and, beyond college, to the people they may want to know some day.

Those were the happiest years we had ever known. I thought we were sitting on a pedestal; I didn't know that what we were really doing was setting ourselves up like tenpins.

It happens to somebody every day. Sometimes it's as direct and as brutal as a mugging. They just shut down the shop and send out the same little slips to everyone from the vice-presidents to the office boys. You sit there saying, "People don't do this sort of thing; not our sort of people, not in this business." But they do and an hour or so later some men in over-alls come around and say, "How about it, Mac; we got orders to move these desks out" and that's your goodbye.

Sometimes you can see it coming. A Mr. Whozit is hired and then a Mr. Whatzit and they start changing things here and there and, perhaps, cutting a few corners. One day you take something into the boss and say, "Look, Harry, we just can't do this," and he says, "Well, I'm sorry you feel that way," and you realize that, for all practical purposes, you have resigned. Sometimes the machines move in and you feel fairly secure because machines, after all, cannot exercise judgment and the firm can hardly eliminate you. You forget it can eliminate judgment.

Sometimes it happens so gently that you can't even be sure it's happening. It's not the political squeeze play; you can fight that because it's aimed right at you. It's a slow-motion reorganization, a revolution on tiptoe which quietly downgrades the job itself until there's not much point in having it held by a man of your experience and salary level. Each change is tiny, much too tiny to be alarming in itself, and you tell yourself that *if* it continues and *when* it reaches this point or that point you'll start looking around. New men appear; young men who seem to be starting near the top and projects bypass your office and end up in theirs. You begin losing your grip and there's nothing you can do about it because nobody's responsible, nobody's knifing you, nobody is doing all this—and everyone is. The responsibility simply drains away from your office like the life-blood from a wounded man. Nobody brings anything in to you any more because there's just nothing to bring; nobody asks you for decisions because there aren't any left to make. There's a technique for everything and the young men—the bright, brittle young men who have never lost anything because they have never loved anything—are trained in the techniques. For some weeks, possibly for some months, you don't know what's happening because you don't want to know. Perhaps you go to them in the end, perhaps they come to you, frequently you're never quite sure whether you resigned or were fired. In any event, it can be done very nicely and there's a cushion of a few weeks or a few months before you actually clean out your desk and leave.

That's the way it happened to me, and they couldn't have been nicer about the whole business. The time came when I felt some problems had to be talked out, and they said, "Well, actually, we're going to handle it a bit differently from now on." This led to a general conversation about various ways and means, and then they were saying, "It's going to be tough on the company, of course, but the last thing in the world we'd want to do is to stand in your way. You've a lot of potential and . . ." with an understanding smile ". . . we couldn't hope to hold on to you forever." I went back to my office convinced that I had resigned, but still feeling funny because it was the first move I had ever faced that wasn't being made strictly on my own initiative. That evening I told Janet and she said, "God dammit, you should have made them fire you!"

This was surprising, coming from Janet. She always liked to see things carried off smoothly, and this had been carried off very smoothly on both sides, but she said, "You're just one of those nice cooperative dopes who helps the executioner adjust the rope and apologizes for getting him up so early in the morning."

"What do you think I should have done," I asked, "started kicking and screaming?"

"Yes, God dammit. You may look pretty dignified to yourself, but you looked like a sucker who was easy to steam-roller to them. There comes a time when people *should* start kicking and screaming."

I let it go at that; there wasn't any point in starting an argument, and I wanted to talk about our vacation.

I had been thinking about it all afternoon. The first two times I had switched jobs I had checked out of one office on a Friday and into another on Monday, and there went the vacation for that year. This time I didn't have to report anyplace on any particular date and it seemed like a good idea to take a break while I could. There wouldn't be another opportunity for at least a year and possibly more.

It would do no harm to spend a few days working out the next step. My most obvious move was to set up a lunch date with Sid. For the past couple of months, he had been tossing out hints which added up to an indirect invitation to change my business cards. If that didn't look good enough, I could follow up three or four other feelers which had come my way recently and spread the word around town that I was available.

That's the way it's done, but on the train that evening, watching the suburban landscape slide by, I wondered if I hadn't dropped into a rut. I felt restless; I felt like a kid who had just been let out of school for the summer vacation. There wasn't any law which said I had to report to Sid; New York was a big city and nobody's bones would be broken if I sniffed around a couple of streets besides Madison Avenue. I thought about that appliance account we'd handled a couple of years before; I probably could have joined their firm as advertising director if I'd wanted to. My mind must have drifted a bit after that, or perhaps I was hypnotized by the flow of landscape past the train window, because I came to with a

start just outside my own station and realized that I had been thinking about Mr. Glenfield and the insurance business. I didn't know
why.

Janet was in favor of a vacation. She was sore at the agency and
hot for squeezing something out of them while I still had the
chance.

"What have you got to lose?" she asked. "You're being booted
out anyway. Tell them you're taking three weeks and I'll bet you a
buck they'll be tickled pink."

At that particular time, I guess, Janet saw some things more
clearly than I did; at any rate, she was right. They seemed a bit
relieved, if anything. I gave her the dollar and told her to blow it
on something she could use in Bermuda.

It was the kids who were upset, since they had to be untangled
from more damn social commitments than I had ever realized they
possessed. Skip would be late getting to camp, and three weeks,
it seemed, would spell the absolute collapse of Cliff's career
in the teen-age division at the yacht club. Cliff settled into a sulk
and this made me a bit sore in turn, since it was the first chance
either of them had ever had to go abroad and I thought they'd be
excited. I tried to placate him by pointing out that he'd have his
own sailboat in a few months—we had agreed that he could have
it at fourteen—but this simply set him to slouching around the
house muttering that I didn't understand.

Despite all this agony, I guess they had a pretty good trip. Cliff
ran into some youngsters of his own age and spent most of his time
with them. Skip made a career of swimming and I got a chance to
talk to Janet about this business of looking around. She saw the
point, all right, but she had some doubts.

"I'm not saying it isn't a good idea," she declared. "I'm just saying there's nothing to stop you from doing it anyway, even if you
do hook up with Sid." Well, this had been her tune when I left that
copywriter's job a good many years before and in those days it had
made sense. At that level, you go by the old axiom: "Don't quit
one job until you have another," because you haven't established
yourself in the business yet and you're just one more young man
tramping in off the street with a scrapbook. As I pointed out to
her, however, I had walked into my new job, climbed into the in-
basket and been smothered with memos from then on. "One week

with Sid," I told her, "and I'll be nailed down for the next five years." We decided that I'd call Sid as soon as we got back, but I wouldn't make any commitments until I'd looked the field over a little.

The vacation must have relaxed me thoroughly because the first thing I noticed when I returned to the office was how nervous everyone seemed and how curtly they talked. Miss Halley was on the phone when I walked in. She hung up quickly and said, "My, you did get a nice tan," and then scooped up a bunch of papers and darted out of the office. That's what I meant, you see, about checking out of one job on Friday and into another on Monday; you don't get your head above water for a single minute. As it was, I felt as if I'd shed ten years.

The first thing I did, before I even looked at the mail, was to phone Sid and set up a lunch date the next day.

I had a cheerful lunch with Sid; a bit too cheerful, perhaps, because I came away with a feeling that I hadn't accomplished very much. I wasn't going to let him pin me down, not at this stage, and I was slightly irked to find that I couldn't pin him down. It was Sid, after all, who had launched the whole business by sounding *me* out and the last couple of times we had met he had been the one to raise the subject. This time we talked about vacations and families and politics and various events around town until it became pretty obvious that he was waiting for me to make the first move and so I did, not too gracefully.

"Talking about vacations," I began, though we hadn't been talking about them at that particular point, "I spent some of my time thinking over that project of yours." Sid said "Oh, yes" brightly and then just sat there waiting for me to continue.

"Why don't we go over it in more detail?" I suggested, and Sid said, "Okay, that's a good idea," but we didn't. It was one of those conversations where the initiative lies with the other person, but he just doesn't pick it up. He answers all your questions, but he doesn't volunteer any information and he doesn't ask any questions in return. You have to keep the ball rolling. In the end I said flatly, "Look, Sid, I'm definitely interested in this." I had to make that point and there wasn't any other way to do it. He said, "That's swell, I knew you would be if I just kept at you long enough," and he added, "Let me give you a call then, sometime next week."

I went back to my office knowing I had been handled and very adroitly. I knew it, and Sid probably knew that I knew it and the question was: Where did I stand now? Perhaps he really did have some project going; perhaps this had just been a peg on which to hang his approach. At any rate, he and his crew had been acting on some definite idea of how I would fit into their operation and now they were revising it. When the offer did come it would be a little less all around—less money, smaller title, less authority. I wouldn't know how much less because no figures had ever been mentioned.

It was pretty obvious that the word was out and I had confirmation of this a couple of days later when a man I knew slightly, the vice-president of a small agency, rang up and asked me to meet him for lunch. "It just seemed to me we were getting out of touch," he said, though we had never been particularly *in* touch, and I nearly turned him down, but what the hell? I went along out of curiosity. There was no fencing this time; he was about as subtle as a housewife buying a sack of potatoes. "We need a good account man," he said, "and we ... ah ... wondered if you'd be interested." I wasn't, especially after I heard the salary they had in mind. This was scavenging, pure and simple; he just thought he'd try his luck at picking off an experienced executive at a bargain price. I had nothing against him or his outfit; I knew enough about them to know that they were good people, but he was asking me to move back eight years and if I couldn't step up, I had to stay even. I had a wife, two kids, two cars and a mortgage. I told him this as diplomatically as I could and he took it cheerfully. "Well, give me a buzz if you change your mind," he said.

There were three more approaches of this sort, one from another agency and two from small companies. The agency spot was a good one and I had a long, serious talk with them. In the end, I said no; I just didn't like the feel of it. There was some talk, for example, of various public relations duties; it was only a casual reference, but I could see myself doing six unrelated jobs and handling none of them well. One company offer would have involved relocation; the other possibility—ad manager for a plastics firm—

|11|

stirred up that off-the-leash restlessness and I took it home that evening to get Janet's reaction. "It means a pay cut," I told her, "but it's not like taking one in the agency field; it could be more in the nature of an investment. I'd be getting a start in a new field." Janet was in one of her suburban farm-girl moods. She was wearing a green and white print dress and she kept poking into a flower pot with one of those miniature garden trowels while I talked. Finally she said, "Well . . ." and at this point Skip came charging in with a busted roller skate he had found behind the garage. We had about ten minutes of no, it can't be fixed and put it back where you found it, dear, and Skip went dragging out looking deprived. I was feeling surprisingly edgy. "Damn it," I said, "this is important."

She shoved a stick into the pot and started fiddling with a piece of string, tying the plant to the stick. When Janet starts fiddling with string or a piece of jewelry or a book of matches, she's usually trying to decide whether to let you have it. She let me have it. "How good an investment was that outfit you're leaving?" she asked.

"Now wait a minute," I said, and Skip came racing in again. I was going to reopen the subject later but the atmosphere didn't seem right and when I got on the train the next morning the matter seemed to have been settled. What I really wanted, perhaps, was the feeling that we had talked this over before I turned down what might be an opportunity. Maybe Mr. Glenfield and those forks in the road were still in my mind. At any rate, I said no again.

AUGUST

"I Didn't Want to Bring It Up in Front of Janet"

The word was out all right. There may be eight million people in New York and nearly two hundred million in the U.S., but any trade is like a small town and nothing stays secret very long. Someone up top mentions it to someone else up top and the news filters down, or the people in your own firm figure it out from the obvious signs and pass it on to friends in other firms, or it simply goes out on the secretary grapevine. Miss Halley had been told officially and she was taking my calls with the air of an Egyptian slave walled up in the tomb of a Pharaoh. Secretaries are terribly sensitive about these things; if their boss is on the skids it rubs off on them, and Miss Halley didn't cherish the idea of being faithful unto death. She may have been sorry to see me go, but since I was going she was counting the days until I checked out.

I suddenly realized there weren't too many of them left.

I'd spent a week getting ready to go away and three weeks on vacation and an additional week which had just drifted past. That left three weeks before I switched addresses. Each day seemed to go by with ghastly slowness and yet every time I looked around another week had slipped away.

I knew I should be more concerned. I knew I should be making phone calls and firing off letters and churning around the city. I went in each morning full of resolution and I puttered away each day with the lists I kept drawing up and revising and the few "general circulation" memoranda they still sent me to keep up appearances. There was very little actual work, but for some reason I went home every night feeling exhausted. The martyred Miss Halley was beginning to get on my nerves and so were a lot of other people. I was being treated as a visitor in a place where I had worked for many years, and I had to keep reminding myself that everyone was really being very nice about the whole business.

Perhaps I'm being a little unfair to Miss Halley. If people have worked with you for a good many years, if they've even put their own jobs on the line at one time or another to back you up, you feel you know them. You forget that friends who will rush to your aid in a fight are likely to keep their distance if you have an infectious disease, and that's the way they see failure. It isn't the danger that drives them away, it's the smell of decay. They shied away from me, too, because there wasn't very much they could say. The world had rolled ahead while I was marking time and, in a few weeks, I had become an outsider.

The calendar jolted me into action. I drew up a list of fifteen names, shook it down to eleven, and split this list into people I would write and people I would phone. Most of the letters were really casual little notes:

Dear Joe:

We were talking a little while back about the problem of new product lines. I've been giving this some thought and, if you're still interested, I think I could help you.

I've felt for a long time, Joe, that the basic trouble lies in the fact that what we call new product promotions are too scattered— this person handles one angle, that person handles another and nobody pulls it together and points it in some effective direction. I've been handling so much new product work in the past couple of years, and I've become so thoroughly immersed in it that I'm seriously considering pushing aside everything else and concentrating on this increasingly important field—provided, of course, that I can settle someplace where I can really put my ideas and experience to work. Why don't we talk it over?

All the best, etc.

|14|

"I Didn't Want to Bring It Up
in Front of Janet"

You wouldn't think that represented a day's work, but it did. By the end of the week I had mailed six such notes and I left the office Friday night with a feeling of accomplishment.

The optimism which springs from activity carried me through a tough Saturday. The toughness was supplied by Janet's brother, Melton, who lived two towns away but usually came over with his wife, Margie, on Saturday afternoon to have supper with us at home or go to the country club dinner dance.

Margie was usually referred to as "a good kid," although she was about thirty-six. She was a bright-eyed little woman who radiated eagerness like a neon sign. "Gee, that would be *wonderful!*" was her favorite line and she could make a few hands of bridge sound like a trip to Paris. Margie was okay; a bit uncomplicated, perhaps, but okay. The mystery was how Melton ever came to marry her, but there has to be a sober side to everyone's life and I guess Melton filled that function for Margie. This may sound as if I didn't get along very well with Melton, but I did. God knows I worked hard enough at it. In some fifteen years, however, I'd never even figured out what to call him. Janet called him "Melly," which was a family nickname and not one I was entitled to use. I had more or less settled on "Mel" which should have rolled off the tongue as easily as "Bill" but didn't for some reason. He didn't like to be called Melton.

Melton was in naval administrative something-or-other in New York during the war and he hooked up with a Wall Street investment firm and stayed on there after he got out of uniform. One of the family's ideas when Janet came east was that Melly could keep an eye on her and he made energetic efforts to do just that. I always had a vague impression that he took Janet's marriage to me as evidence that he had fallen down on the job. Melton was okay, too, I guess. If I could have had one good row with him each year we would have gotten along beautifully the rest of the time.

Margie managed to mislay both sets of car keys that night, so they got off to a late start and met us at the club. Two minutes after we sat down, Melton stood up again and announced that he was going to the men's room. "You coming, too?" he asked me. This was meant to sound casual, but a casual Melton was like a waltzing elephant. I went along and as soon as we got into the corridor he asked, "What's this about you being fired? I didn't want to bring it up in front of Janet."

|15|

"Don't be an idiot," I told him. "Janet knows."

"Well," he said, "it isn't a very pleasant thing to talk about at table." That was what I always found fascinating about my brother-in-law—you could count on him to do the wrong thing, but he was meticulous about doing it the right way.

"Look, Mel," I said. "If we've got to talk about it, let's wait until we get home. Besides, you've got it backward. I didn't get fired. I'm just switching jobs, like I did before."

I turned to go back, but Melton wasn't going to leave it at that. "Where are you going?" he wanted to know. "What have you switched to?" I thought of a couple of good answers to that one but, as I said, I put a good deal of effort into getting along with Melton.

"I'll tell you later," I answered. "We'll talk it over when we get home. It isn't fair to the girls to leave them stranded at the table like that." So we went back and sat down and then Melton discovered he really did have to go to the men's room. Before the evening ended, I figured out what was wrong. In Mel's world, nice people didn't get fired; there was something disreputable about it.

Sunday was a clear, hot day. I mixed a drink and took it out to the patio and sat there soaking up the sun. New York and the ad business were a light year away. I was a copra trader, sitting on the veranda of my home in Tahiti and gazing out over my plantation. The house, the yard, the garage—they were solid, they were real. A few words spoken in an office in New York weren't going to destroy them.

That was Sunday. Monday I launched my telephone campaign and by Wednesday I'd heard more than a few words, none of them put together in the right combinations:

"I'm very glad you called. It's been interesting to talk to you. We've been thinking along the same lines and it's possible that we may set up something in the fall. If you're still available . . ."

"As a matter of fact, I don't handle that any more. They brought in this guy . . ."

"Well, you know; things are pretty slow in the summer . . ."

"Why yes, we are going ahead with it, but on a slightly smaller scale than we'd originally planned. To tell you the truth, we're looking for a man who . . . well, someone who's, let's say . . ."

Younger. Younger and cheaper. You hear a lot of talk about

this over-forty business, of course, but I never paid very much attention to it. I'd always pegged it in my own mind on the sort of man who's a has-been at forty-two. Everyone knows a couple of these guys—they're good enough to get by, but they haven't got what it takes to climb, and by the time they're forty problems begin to crop up: bottle-knocking or skirt-chasing or job-hopping, or just plain incompatibility with the team. This hardly described a man who had made something of a mark in his business and these people were being just a little bit stupid if they thought they were dealing with that kind of guy. If it came to that, I could haul out my scrapbook and point to clippings from trade books and newspaper business sections: the speeches I'd made, the award I'd received, stuff like that. These things didn't cut any ice by themselves, of course, the important thing was that they reflected the self-awareness, the sense of direction which a man should have by the time he's forty.

I was still boiling when Miss Halley brought in the mail. There was an envelope on top with the return address of Joe's firm in the corner. I ripped it open and pulled out the letter:

Dear Sir:

Mr. —————— has asked me to express his regret that there is no opening available in this organization at the moment. Should one occur at some date in the future we would, of course, be glad to consider your application for employment.

Sincerely yours,

Laura L. Banks
Secretary.

I looked at the envelope. It was addressed to me. I read the letter again.

Application for employment!

I told Miss Halley to get Joe on the phone. Somebody—the chilly Miss Banks, perhaps—obviously had goofed and turned my letter over to the personnel department before Joe had seen it. If nothing else, he ought to know if people were taking liberties with his name. I had known Joe for some years and he might tell someone to go jump in the lake, but he had never "expressed his regret" about anything. Miss Halley mumbled into the phone for a couple of minutes and then hung up. "He's in conference," she said. "I left a message that you called."

I made two more efforts to get through to Joe, one Wednesday afternoon and the second Thursday morning as soon as I got in. I gave up after I'd had a look at Thursday's mail. There were three replies and one of them was worded in virtually the same language as Joe's little contribution. I might have been applying for a job as an office boy.

The others were more encouraging, at first glance. Jerry —— had written: "I think your ideas make a lot of sense and we'll have to get together and go over them in more detail. Hope Janet and the boys are doing well. Give them my best." This sounded fine until I realized that it didn't really say anything beyond an implied promise to talk to me personally. After those two freeze-outs, however, it was like an award. It occurred to me at this point that I hadn't heard from Sid, so I gave him a call and felt a chill when Miss Halley reported that he was in conference. He really was tied up, however, because he phoned back an hour later and apologized. "It's been one of those weeks," he said, "and I haven't had much of a chance to talk to anyone about you. Let me get in touch with you sometime around the middle of next week."

Was I expecting to have a red carpet rolled out for me? You're damn right I was, and for two reasons: I might be hunting for a job, but I was also offering something—fifteen years of hard-won experience.

I felt I rated special consideration, too, because I had always given it. If an adman called me for an interview, he got one, not because I was a nice guy, but because he was a fellow professional. I seldom had the time to do this, but I made the time because this was one of the things you had to do to earn that title "professional." I had done it for them: now I was asking them to do it for me.

When the weekend arrived, however, I could see the bright side. I took a drink out to the patio again and sat there, surveying my plantation and thinking that the balance sheet didn't look too bad. At least five approaches had been made to me, even if four of them were unsatisfactory, and at least seven of the ten approaches I had made had received sympathetic consideration. It was not the number but the nature of those turn-downs which had jolted me. I wondered what the hell Joe thought he was going to say the first time he ran into me after I'd settled down someplace else, and then a thought belted me right between the eyes. For whatever reasons, Joe obviously didn't expect me to settle down someplace else.

By evening I was feeling depressed again.

Janet said, somewhat tentatively, "It's not going very well, is it?" and I answered, "Oh, well, things are always slow in the summer." I hadn't told her about those two curt replies and in this, perhaps, I did her an injustice. I had some idea of preserving the basic security of my home and some small sense of pride in the belief that my working problems would never reach the point where Janet, let alone the kids, would ever be affected by them. At odd moments throughout the weekend, though, I would writhe as if someone had jabbed me with a red-hot iron. Those notes, those goddam, contemptuous, snotty notes.

I think Janet sensed that something had gone sour, though she saw I didn't want to talk about it and she didn't press the point. Melly sensed it, too, and Melly wasn't a boy who could be steered tactfully away from a touchy topic, not even in the middle of our Saturday night bridge game. "I thought you had something all lined up," he said.

"Maybe yes, maybe no," I told him. "I'll keep you posted. It's your deal, Marge."

"Oh, dear, are you sure?" Marge hated to deal.

"I just wonder if you're doing everything you could be doing," Melly said. "Have you written a résumé?"

"I've written six résumés," I said, trying to sound final without sounding rude. "I'm pretty sure it's your deal, Marge," I added. "I'm afraid I lost track. Maybe it's Mel's turn."

"There's a bookkeeper in our office," Mel continued doggedly, "who worked for one of Those Places Uptown and lost his job in some merger. He sat down and drew up a list of fifty firms—fifty, mind you—and then he wrote a darn good résumé and mailed a copy off to everyone on the list. Got a dozen offers, just like that."

"I'll deal," said Janet suddenly. "Would you pass me those cards, Melly?"

"Huh?"

"Those cards by your elbow, could I have them?"

"Oh . . . sure. Now in your case . . ."

|19|

"Anyone want another drink?" Marge asked brightly.

"Oh, hell," I said. "Let's straighten this out and get on with the game. This little gimmick of yours probably could land me a job, Mel—as a bookkeeper. The sort of job I have . . . had . . . just isn't one you go after that way. If you must know, I do have a list but it's a list of people I know and people who know me. And I don't mail them résumés and say 'I'm unemployed, please hire me.' I write them letters and say something positive—I want to do a certain sort of work for them or something like that. Okay, it's a slow business but I can't help that; this is the way you get anything worthwhile. The day I start plastering the landscape is the day I haven't got any professional position left and if that happens I'm in real trouble and so's this house and so's that Scotch you're drinking. All clear now?"

I could see it wasn't, but Janet was dealing the cards, flicking them around the table with a brisk snap, snap, snap, and Marge was bustling back and forth with drinks and the subject had been closed so obviously that not even Melly could pry it open again. I could have stuffed those cards down his throat though because I was in trouble by my own definition, and so was the house and so was the Scotch. For a few moments, concentrating on the cards, I had forgotten about Joe and about Sid and about those damn notes.

Well, the hell with all of them, and that included Miss Halley. When she slithered in Monday morning with the mail I told her I was going out to buy a new suit.

"Hadn't you better just glance through these first?" she asked, holding out a handful of envelopes. I walked over to the door and picked my hat off the rack. "Sit on them, Miss Halley," I said. "Maybe you'll hatch something." I paused in the lobby to give Joyce, the gorgeous receptionist, the word. "I'm going out to buy a new suit," I told her. "I'll be back in about a year." Joyce gave me her Number Two smile and said "Why, certainly."

I've always hated buying clothes, but this time it was a party. I looked over the suits with the eye of an earl, picked one out and deliberately refrained from asking the price. The fitter's efforts to terrorize me, which were usually pretty successful, failed utterly; I snapped at him until both he and the salesman were spilling "sirs" like medieval retainers. On the crest of this sudden arrogance I went from the tailor to the barber and from there to an expensive restaurant where I stewed up a storm until I got a table which suited me. After a leisurely lunch, I strolled back to the office to find that Sid had called. It completed my wonderful morning to think that he hadn't been able to reach me.

Sid was crisp and businesslike when I returned his call. "I've got another stinking week," he announced, "but we're getting things sorted out. Can you have lunch with Abe and me Thursday?" There was a positive ring in his voice which said that everything had been settled and everything was going to be okay, so I said, sure, fine, and hung up. That was that, and in an odd sort of way I felt a bit sorry because it seemed more or less inevitable that I would switch over to Sid's shop, and I still had a feeling that there was a good deal of territory between his office and mine which I could have spent those eight weeks exploring.

Tuesday and Wednesday brought an odd little outburst of work, as if the firm had suddenly realized that it had only a few more days left in which to use my services. I did it conscientiously if somewhat wryly; the eight weeks grace period had been granted under an implied agreement that I wouldn't slam the door when I left, and, since I was going to be working only a few streets away there was no point launching feuds at the last moment. This eleventh-hour panic was a little amusing; I'd thought they were all set to carry on without me. On Thursday I went to meet Sid and his boss.

Sid's boss was a great man for boats and we talked boats. Cliff's yacht club activities had provided me with some sailing jargon and I trotted it out, but Abe was a cruising man. "It's great stuff for kids, this sailing," he admitted. "It teaches them a hell of a lot. But until you've lived on a boat . . ." and he launched into a long account of a trip down the inland waterways to Florida. We finished our lunch and the coffee came and Abe stopped talking suddenly, right in the middle of an encounter with a drawbridge. He looked at Sid and that was Sid's cue to speak his piece.

"Well," said Sid. "Here's the way it is. You know how things are and I may as well come to the point and say that we feel, after talking it over, that we don't want to get involved in any new proj-

|21|

ects right now. In the fall, perhaps, or after the first of the year, the picture may be a lot different. At the same time, we definitely want you to come in with us . . ."

"Definitely," said Abe.

". . . so the problem is, where can we fit you in? Now I'm sure that in the future we'll see our way clear to use your abilities the way we know they ought to be used, but right now . . ." Then he put forward their offer. It was just about the same offer which that small agency had made a couple of weeks before.

You'd think the money would be the main point, but my first reaction, once again, was "That's where I was eight years ago." What became of those eight years and all the work which went into them? The dollars made the decision, however—I simply couldn't afford to take such a job. Sid was just sitting there, staring at me, and Abe was stirring his coffee with an air of vast concentration, punctuating the silence with his spoon's clink, clink, clink.

"I'm sorry, Sid," I said finally. "I'd like to come in with you and I'd stretch a point to do it. But I can't stretch it that far."

Sid looked at Abe and he nodded.

"Well," said Sid. "If you came in on those terms now and if things worked out, which I'm sure they would, we could probably see our way clear to improving the financial end somewhat within a year." That didn't help much, since "somewhat" wouldn't bridge the gap and there was still the other difficulty, the fact that they weren't going to need the most important areas of my experience. Putting it all together, I saw how a man could slide downhill. A year or so in a job which didn't make use of his training and it could atrophy, it could become outdated, and then he wouldn't be fit for anything better. I'd spent my whole life grabbing for experience and never quite getting caught up and now, suddenly, I had too much and nobody wanted to buy it.

"No," I said. "I'm sorry to put it this way, Sid, but I may as well be honest. I can obviously do better."

Abe looked relieved. "I know you can," he said. "And Sid and I will be kicking ourselves a year from now. It's just the way things are at the moment."

Friday I finished cleaning out my desk. There wasn't much to clean out, since I had been pulling stuff out of it for several weeks and very little had been coming in. When I finished it was bare and

you could see all the nicks and scratches. It looked empty and battered, like a desk in a second-hand furniture store. There didn't
seem to be much point in spending the afternoon behind it and
I felt a bit funny about going out with the crowd at 5:30, so I
said what goodbyes there were to be said and cleared out at
four. Miss Halley surprised me by saying "It's awful; I think it's
just awful," which was nice of her because it enabled me to leave
the office without feeling that I was just someone who had come
in to look at the plumbing. I stopped on the street corner for a
moment to look back at the building which held such a large chunk
of my thirties, but there wasn't anything I could take away with
me. It was just a square glass box, like a hundred other Madison
Avenue buildings.

I spent most of the weekend sitting on the patio but I didn't
have much luck being a Tahitian planter. On Monday I got up and
shaved and had breakfast and dressed and drove the small car
down to the station. I picked up a morning paper as usual and
spent the first half hour or so of the trip in reading it. I was more
than half way to New York before I realized that I didn't know
where I was going.

"We May Be Undergoing Some Expansion in the Future"

Somebody once claimed that you could spend your whole life in Grand Central Station and never have to come out. This is pretty close to the truth; Grand Central is a miniature city and you can do nearly anything there from going to the movies to getting your suit pressed. For all of this, however, it was less use to me than one lousy little office would have been, with a desk and a secretary to shove calls through in the proper manner.

Still, that was as far as the train went.

I stepped into the stream of commuters flowing up the ramp and bumped into whatzizname, the guy who sometimes stopped by the house with his fifteen-year-old boy to give Cliff a lift down to the yacht club. Barney Epstein. He had a small public relations agency called Something or Other Associates and seemed to make a good thing out of it.

Epstein had the yacht club on his mind and he wanted to ask if Cliff and I would be at some father-and-son meeting there the following Saturday. I told him, sure, we wouldn't miss it, and he said that was fine because they were going to talk about plans for the following year. We reached the top of the ramp and he added, "I'll give you a lift uptown; I go right past your place." Epstein may have known I was leaving, but he apparently didn't know I had left.

"No, thanks," I told him. "I'm heading straight downtown. Got an early appointment."

After that, of course, I had to tramp over toward the Lexington Avenue side to get away from him. I looked into the window of a book store for about five minutes and then backtracked to a small restaurant, where I sat down at a table and ordered a cup of coffee. I was pretty sore at myself.

I was sore because I had made no real effort Friday to set up something for Monday. I was sore because I hadn't spent the weekend overhauling my notes and my list of phone numbers. I was sore because, looking back over the past eight weeks, it seemed to me that I had simply dribbled this valuable time away. An office and a secretary, a good business address, I'd had them and I hadn't done a damn thing with them, apart from two brief outbursts of activity. What I wanted now was that eight-week period to live over again.

I had worried about the future, but I hadn't visualized it. Somehow I'd always seen myself sitting in an office, someplace; there hadn't been any mental picture of me marooned in a coffee shop and wondering what to do and where to go next.

The waitress flicked at the table-top with her napkin. I ordered another cup of coffee and then opened my attaché case and laid my notes out on the table. When I'd looked them over I felt a little better. There were at least three letters asking me to call, if you counted Jerry's "We must get together." I turned an envelope over, listed the names and phone numbers on the back and then asked the cashier for a dollar's worth of nickels and dimes.

There were several phone booths on the opposite side of the station. I laid the envelope on the little ledge in one of them and put my pen and an extra dime on top of it and then I dialed Jerry's number. His secretary put me right through and he said, "Hi, there."

"Hi, Jerry. Look, about that note I wrote you. I find I can crack loose this afternoon, so why don't we make it today if that's all right with you?"

It sounded phony as hell to me, coming from a phone booth in Grand Central, but Jerry said, "How about three o'clock?" It was on the tip of my tongue to ask him if he could make it for lunch,

|25|

but I decided not to push my luck. "That's fine," I answered, "I'll see you at three."

So far so good. I dialed the next number on my list.

"I'm sorry," said a brisk secretarial voice, "but he's out of his office at the moment. I expect him in about an hour. Can he call you back?" I glanced automatically at the number on the dial and then remembered that he couldn't, not unless I spent the day in the phone booth. I had read someplace that small-time bookies do stake out phone booths and use them as offices. All I had to do, if my memory were correct, was to settle down with a couple of hot dogs and a few magazines and pretend I was talking on the phone if somebody started hanging around outside.

"No thanks," I said, "I'll call again." I hung up.

That phone booth was the first thing which made me feel "unemployed" instead of "available." It led me into all sorts of small stratagems. I had to say, "No thanks, I'll call back" again on my second call, and during my third I had to feed a dime into the slot during the conversation. Something about this simple act was terribly humiliating. I had made enough business calls from phone booths in the past, but I hadn't made them on this sort of business. I tried to sound confident, but that tinny "ding, ding" as the dime dropped through said that this guy was a phony; his headquarters were in his hat and his office had been rented for three minutes from the New York Telephone Company, lease renewable for another ten cents.

It was nearly noon when I finished my calls. I stepped out of the phone booth and started toward the street, but half way there I turned back and stood staring at the phones. I wanted to have lunch with somebody. I didn't care who it was, I just didn't want to eat alone. I was feeling the first twinge of that terrible loneliness which haunts the unemployed; I wanted to share a table with someone who knew me and knew who I was and what I was.

On a sudden impulse I called Epstein and suggested that we get together. "I've sort of lost touch with Cliff's activities at the yacht club," I explained. "Running into you this morning reminded me of it. I feel bad about it but you know how it is; you get so jammed up." Epstein sounded surprised, but he said okay and I walked out on to Lexington Avenue feeling a lot more cheerful. Lunch was booked and the afternoon was booked and I had two appointments for Tuesday.

Epstein spent an hour talking about the junior sailing program; it was one of his major enthusiasms. "When Cliff gets his boat, you'll probably be spending a lot more time down there," he said somewhat wistfully, and I realized that he must have a tough time getting other parents to help with the work. The coffee came and I asked him how his business was going. "Good," he answered, "very good," but he suddenly looked tired. "Sometimes I wish it would slow down. The more we make, the faster we have to run. It's like racing down a long hill in a car with no brakes; you're okay as long as you keep swinging that steering wheel, but you can't take your eye off the road for a moment. Running a small business these days . . ." and he shook his head.

"You could always quit if you had to," I pointed out. "With your experience, one of the big outfits . . ."

There was a funny look on Epstein's face—a sort of comic grimness.

"No thanks," he said. "Most things are that way these days and I'd rather be holding the wheel than riding in the back seat. I get a certain sense of personal security out of that. I'd rather be my own failure than somebody else's deadwood."

The waiter brought the check and Epstein reached for it, but I took it out of his hand. After all, the lunch had been my idea. It was past two o'clock when we left the restaurant and, with a stroll up Madison Avenue, I could just about make that three o'clock date with Jerry comfortably. I stopped on the way and bought a couple of neckties to go with my new suit. There were some nice-looking tie-clips in the shop and, on an impulse, I blew four bucks on one and put it on immediately.

The session with Jerry was a long one. We talked for half an hour or so, mainly about new products, and then he said, "Why don't we bounce some of this off The Man?" as if the idea had just occurred to him. He buzzed his secretary and asked her to find out if the boss was in and could spare a moment. The boss was and he could. It was all very offhand, but I was pretty sure it had been set up so The Man could have a look at me and I was glad I had bought the new tie-clip. We went into the front office where Jerry introduced me to a chunky, tough-looking little man who shook my hand and then sat down and waited silently for me to begin. It was obviously going to be more of a presentation than a conversation and I wasn't prepared for this. I kicked myself for being caught off guard, but I did my best to cover the points I had made in my chat with Jerry and give them a beginning, a middle and a quick end. When I had finished The Man glanced at Jerry and then stood up and shook my hand again.

"Very interesting," he said. "Thank you very much. I'm glad you could drop in."

That glance was what chilled me; I was beginning to recognize it and it meant "This may be all very well, but where could we fit this guy in?" Jerry said essentially the same thing when we got back to his office, though he wrapped it up as thoroughly as possible. "I think the boss liked you," he told me. "He always clams up like that when he likes somebody; he's afraid he might say something which could be taken as a commitment. We do have some projects marinating and we may need some expert help in a couple of months or so. Right now . . ."

"I'm not in any hurry, Jerry," I said. "I want to look the field over and settle in some place where I can do some good. I'll keep in touch with you, if you don't mind, and we'll see if anything works out." I picked up my hat and attaché case and he walked out to the elevator with me. "Take it easy," he said, "and give my best to Janet and the kids."

I glanced at my watch. It was 4:45 and there was a 5:05 train but it would be better to wait an hour and travel with the commuting crowd. You never knew who you might run into. I dawdled along Madison Avenue, looking in shop windows, down to the Grand Central area. Half an hour left to kill. I went into a drug store and spent twenty minutes or so leafing through paperback books. There were several best-sellers which I hadn't read; in the end, however, I settled on a collection of mystery stories.

At train time I walked the length of the platform, peering hopefully into each car through the windows, without spotting any familiar faces. I finally picked a seat at random and opened the book, but after the train pulled out of the station I closed it again and tried to think.

It had been a big day in our lives when we moved out of a Manhattan apartment and into our own home, but, at this point, I envied the men who lived in the city. They had their headquarters right on the scene; they could reach any office building from their home in a few minutes. They could make phone calls without difficulty and, even more important, receive them. I had spent one day—just one day—on the loose in New York and this business of killing time between appointments already was beginning to rasp on my nerves. New York is not organized for the idle or contemplative man. Paris has its sidewalk cafes, London its parks, but New Yorkers use their streets only to get from one place to another.

Could I borrow somebody's apartment for a week or so? I turned over some names, but I wouldn't care to ask anyone but a close friend and virtually all our close friends lived in the suburbs. I belonged to several clubs, but most of them were luncheon groups with no permanent premises of their own and using a club, in any event, would mean advertising my rootlessness among the very people I was trying to impress. The thought of renting desk space crossed my mind but I dismissed it as ridiculous; it amounted to organizing a temporary job hunt as a sort of permanent corporate enterprise.

Still, some active organizing had to be done; that was obvious. Something should have clicked by now, but nothing had; the whole business was becoming too complicated to carry in my head and in odd notes on the back of envelopes. A program, a planned approach, that's what was needed now, and the first step was to sift through my files and list everyone I had contacted, should contact or might contact. I'd begin right after dinner.

Janet was waiting at the station with the small car and her own collection of questions. The big car was "doing that thing again" and she'd left it at the garage. "For God's sake," I said, "we paid fifty bucks to have that fixed just last month." The butcher's bill was wrong and the butcher insisted that it was correct. She had tried to reason with Cliff about some small shortcoming and he had slammed out of the house without answering her.

"Okay," I said wearily, ignoring the rest and answering the last point. "I'll speak to him." We turned off the main highway into our road and Janet asked, "How did it go today?"

"Not too badly. I saw Jerry and he sent you his best. Oh, and I had lunch with Epstein . . ."

"Who?"

"Epstein, the yacht club man. I have to go to a meeting there with Cliff Saturday."

|29|

"Don't forget that Margie and Melly are coming over early on Saturday," said Janet. A moment later she asked, "How did you come to have lunch with Epstein?" but we were turning into the driveway and I let the question slide. Janet went into the kitchen and I made an effort to smooth things over with Cliff. I didn't have much luck; he answered my questions with grunts and then sulked through supper. After the meal had dragged to a gloomy end, I carried my attaché case into the living room and opened it. I was feeling pretty damned exhausted. The paperback book was in there and, after a moment's hesitation I picked it out and settled back to read. After all, there were two appointments on Tuesday.

Janet drove me to the station in the morning. "Something's going to have to be done about that boy," she began, as we turned out of the driveway, but I fended off this subject.

"Look, honey, I'm pretty worried about him myself, but right now—this week, I mean—I'm going to have to concentrate on digging out a few more leads. I should have done it last night and I've got to get at it tonight."

"I thought you said this business with Jerry and his boss was going pretty well?"

"I said it was encouraging, but just the same I want to get cracking."

"Of course you do," she replied sympathetically. "I just hate to see you getting so worried. I mean; you've only been out of work for one day."

Sometimes, I think, you get maddest at the people you love when they reflect your own weaknesses.

"One day! I've been out of the *office* for one day but I've been looking for two Goddam *months*. God dammit, Janet, will you get that through your head? Two months and I haven't done a damn thing but sit around and wait for something to happen! I can't go on fumbling away time like this."

"Of course you can't," she said in the tone reserved for cut fingers. "But you haven't just been sitting around. There was all that business with Sid and it wasn't your fault that that didn't work out and then there were those other offers and everything."

She had me feeling a lot better by the time we reached the station though I repeated again, as I opened the car door, that dammit we had to get organized and we were going to begin that night.

"By the way," she said, "I want to ask something. Is there any way I can reach you during the day if something comes up? Where are you hanging out between appointments?"

She just didn't realize, that was all.

My first appointment was at 9:30 and I was back in the street by 10:15. I talked with two vice-presidents, a sort of Abbott and Costello team with the habit of completing or confirming each other's remarks. They were pleasant, brief and brisk. "I think I should tell you," said Abbott, "that we have no openings here. None at all."

"At present," amended Costello.

"However, there's a possibility . . ."

"A good possibility," said Costello.

". . . that we may be undergoing some expansion in the future. Of course by that time you might not be interested, but . . . uh . . ."

". . . on the other hand, you might," finished Costello.

They led through a fast, searching review of my background. It was all done with a smile—Abbott, in fact, leaned back and put his feet on his desk—but it was all done quite expertly. By 10 o'clock they had pumped me thoroughly and Abbott put his feet down and said, "Like to have a look around the shop?" This, too, was conducted with leisurely speed. "Art department," said Costello, opening one door. "Art director," he added, pointing to a shirt-sleeved man sitting behind a scarred desk. I was introduced and Abbott tapped me on the shoulder. "Something across the hall here which will interest you," he suggested and we were off again. We wound up at the elevators in slightly less than fifteen minutes and both men shook hands enthusiastically. "Glad you could drop by," said Abbott. "Keep in touch," said Costello. Riding down in the elevator I decided that I liked those people. There was an air of professionalism in the office which suggested that they got a great deal of work done and had a lot of fun besides. The outfit had been near the bottom of my list but I moved it up a few places.

I had a lunch date at 12:30 and an appointment at three. There were two hours to get through, two hours' confinement on the street which would seem like a week in a cell. With a sudden surge of determination, I walked over to the Public Library, trudged up the steps between the haughty stone lions, and spread out my papers

|31|

on a table in one of the reading rooms. I worked for more than an hour on what might be called an operations notebook, listing the people I still had to contact and the people I had already seen, with a brief summary of each interview. On a separate page I began a follow-up sheet—"call Jerry Friday," and so on—setting down each firm in order of priority, the hot prospects first, then the "maybes" such as Abbott and Costello. By noon I had done as much as I could without my files, so I went outside and sat on the steps in the sunshine with a smug awareness that I had earned a half hour's idleness.

At 12:15 I stood up, dusted off the seat of my pants and went to meet Phil for lunch. The restaurant was one we both knew well and I threw my usual greeting at the headwaiter as I walked in: "Hi, Philippe. Where have you hidden Mr. Carhill today?" He ignored me, or appeared to, until I asked again.

"M'sieu was expecting someone?" There was no flicker of recognition on his face.

I repeated the name and he consulted his reservations list. "I 'ave no gentleman of that name . . ." he began, but at that point I spotted Phil at the bar. Perhaps Philippe had merely been rushed —the lunch crowd *was* pouring in—but headwaiters have a sixth sense about these things. You may be wearing two-hundred-dollar shoes, but they can see the skids under the soles. Well, what the hell; it wasn't the only restaurant in town. I sat down beside Phil and ordered a drink.

Phil was an old friend, a maverick who started his career in my first agency but split off to go into industrial sales. A salesman, he often said, led the unloved life of an orphaned camel, but on one occasion when I had tried to coax him back into advertising he had laughed and shaken his head. "A smart fish," he said mysteriously, "prefers the roughest water to the smoothest air." His trademark was an enormous, battered briefcase which he never let out of his sight. It was leaning against the bar stool as I walked up and he moved it aside with a casual kick to make room for my feet.

"What are you drinking?" he asked. He signaled the bartender, and then added, "So you got bounced from that Madison Avenue aquarium of yours?"

"I resigned from the agency, if that's what you mean."

"If you left and you didn't want to leave, you were **bounced**. Is anyone waiting with open arms?"

I gave him a brief rundown on the previous few weeks and he
shook his head. "You should talk to a salesman, my friend, before
you set out to sell something; I could have told you how the theme
song runs." He began to drum on the bar with his hands. "I'm
going to set it to music and call it 'The Next Year Blues':
    'Oh, de costs is high, de profits is low
    'Swing your salesmen and do-ci-do!' "
Philippe came over to announce that our table was ready. It was
a typical mid-Manhattan restaurant with less than a foot between
tables and we interrupted conversations on both sides as we
squeezed into the tiny chairs. A sleek young man on my right
glared at me and lowered his voice. I could still catch an occasional word. "Prestructured" was one of them and another was
"inwardized." I felt old and a bit rumpled.

"Things are always slow in the summer," I told Phil. "I'm not
going to fly into a panic about that."

"Ah, but they are not slow. They are booming. They are booming so beautifully, in fact, that nobody wants to rock the boat. If
the booming continues to boom—and I quote from many recognized authorities in my territory—we are going to do magnificent
things next year. Meanwhile, just put me down for the standard
order."

"Phil," I said, "I've known you for fifteen years and I've never
known a time when the world wasn't going to hell in a hand-
basket."

"I didn't say that. I'm just giving you a piece of advice. Look
for people who are doing things today; don't wait around for the
ones with big plans for tomorrow. You take my home town.
They've got a picture hanging up in the railroad station; an artist's
conception of a magnificent new railway terminal. Everyone in
town is proud as hell of it; they talk about the new terminal this
and the new terminal that and it's more real to them than the one
which is actually standing there. *That* happens to be falling apart,
but they look at it and they don't even see it, they see the new
terminal."

Phil picked up his menu and studied it for a moment. "That picture's been hanging there for twenty years," he added.

"Phil," I said, "if you hate selling so much why don't you get
out of it?"

He finished off his drink and looked at me with a grin. "I don't

|33|

get out of it because I'm good at it. Basically, I'm several things.
I'm what your people would call a small-picture man, for one. I'm
the sort of guy who would mow a lawn by snipping off each blade
of grass with a pair of nail scissors. I like details; I think they can
be important. Is this good or bad?"

"Well . . ." I began, but Phil plowed ahead.

"The answer is: it depends where I'm working. In that agency,
as I found out, it was bad. Where I work now, it's good." Phil gave
his briefcase another kick. "They wouldn't let me in that agency
with this," he added, "but it's my badge. Every scar on it is a dollar in my pocket. I walk into some of these plants and they say,
'Hey Phil, we're having some trouble; got anything in the briefcase
that'll help?' Well, I usually do because I stuff everything in there
which might possibly be of some use to my customers."

"So all the time you were in advertising," I said, "you were a
sort of mute, inglorious Milton of sales."

"Got nothing to do with advertising or sales. It's the attitude of
the company itself. I was a square peg in a bottle-neck because
that was the kind of outfit that put up with its employees. They
used to look over a guy and say, 'It's too bad he's this and that,
we'll just have to make the best of it.' Another firm, now; it might
look at these things as possible bonuses and figure out how it could
use them."

The waiter swooped near our table and we trapped him long
enough to order some coffee.

"You know," Phil continued, reflectively, "it takes a lot of
things—personality traits and training and so on—to make up one
human being. The way I figure it, if you work for some outfit and
too many of those things are either useless or liabilities, then get
the hell out. I'm a great believer in hard work, but you could work
your tail off digging for gold in the middle of Times Square and
still hit nothing but sewer pipes. You've got to dig, but it helps if
you dig where the gold is."

At home that evening I took out my operations notebook and
tried to work on it, but I couldn't concentrate. There was a pattern
some place and I couldn't quite grasp it; there was an answer
which kept eluding me. I had seen a lot of people, pulled a lot of
strings, used my entree to a lot of offices and what I had was a
haze of half-promises and future projects. Despite the handshakes,

the lunches and the long discussions, I couldn't bring anyone to the point of actually saying "Sit down and go to work." I couldn't make anything *move*. Something always seemed to be on the verge of clicking; nothing actually did.

At that moment I felt my first touch of panic. What was I, really, but a miscellaneous bundle; a scrapbook, an award, a few years' experience and a handful of what we liked to call "contacts?" How many other men like me were wandering around New York, dropping dimes in phone boxes and trying to make themselves felt in three minutes?

I went out to the kitchen, got some ice cubes from the refrigerator and poured myself a drink. Walking back through the living room, I pulled myself together. The walls, the furniture, the bookcases; they looked solid and reassuring. The hurricane hadn't swept away the old plantation yet.

I settled down to work, plowing through my files and picking names from old letters, old memoranda and occasionally from my memory when it was jogged by some scrap of paper. By midnight I felt tired but satisfied; I had compiled an impressive list and I was ready to start stage two of the search in the morning.

In the morning? I glanced at the clock and decided, as a token of my determination, to launch it immediately, at least to the extent of one letter. I rolled a sheet of paper into the typewriter and began:

Dear Mr. ————————
You may recall our interesting chat at the convention last year when you mentioned your problems with. . . .

|35|

"Didn't You Feel There Was a Good Future Where You Were?"

The time had come to make this a family project.

"I'm sorry," I said rather helplessly to Janet. "I thought it would be all settled by this time. If that thing with Sid had worked out . . ."

"But something could still click tomorrow; any day," she said.

That was the hump I'd had to climb over and now I had to help her over it. "Sure it could, but we can't count on it any longer. Something's gone sour. I don't know whether it's me or things generally or what, but we've got to quit saying that something could click tomorrow. It could be another month or so and we'd better start cutting back."

"There's always the country club," she suggested. "We could give it up, I mean. And some of the boys' activities, they're pretty expensive."

I said yes to the country club and no to the idea of restricting the kids. We dropped a good deal of cash at the club, one way or another. The drinks were expensive and so were those Saturday night dinners—especially since Melly's attitude toward picking up the tab stopped somewhere short of eagerness. We could save a respectable chunk of money by simply staying away and the only question was What Would People Think?

This was a business question, not a social one. We'd moved to the suburbs in the first place to be near the right crowd and now we were stuck with it. For the sake of appearances, for the sake of my search, we had to keep mixing.

We had to, but we couldn't. The figures decided that point. The time had come to start saving cash even if it meant losing face.

A good many decisions of this sort had to be tackled. One jolt came from the discovery that unemployment can be expensive. I couldn't save on clothes, for example, not if I was going to put up a good appearance. What about drinks at Philippe's? I ran into Harry there and fed him the whole package: how I was taking my time; how I was fending off the anguished appeals of firms which weren't worthy of my services. As far as I could see, Harry soaked it all up; he still believes there is such a world. With guys like Harry, however, money is the ultimate test of authenticity and I had to be quite firm about picking up the check. The fact that I could pick it up without wincing was one measure of my progress. Anyone can tell lies, but financing them takes a certain touch of sincerity.

Of all these decisions, the one which rammed my nose deepest into the time vs. money dilemma was the cost of commuting. If I stayed home I wasted a day. If I went into the city and accomplished nothing, I had thrown away the cash equivalent of a day on my fare and other expenses. I decided to keep on commuting on the theory—admittedly a negative one—that nothing was going to move if I camped at home.

As for the kids, what the hell could I do? A lot of the money we spent and a lot of the things we bought for them were linked with their activities. It's one thing to ask a child to go without a toy; it's quite another to cut him off from his friends and restrict his life. There was the constant taxiing to various dates and events, for example, plus the problem of Cliff's boat. I could only hope that I caught on someplace before that particular decision came up.

"I'm beginning to wonder," I said to Janet, "if it wasn't a mistake to turn down those offers. I could have been looking around and we would have had something coming in, at least."

"Maybe some of them are still open," she suggested. Well, maybe they were, but I liked the idea even less after my lunch with Phil. If they can't use your abilities, stay out, he had advised, and he was right—provided you could afford to choose. If a man can't bring his talents and his experience to bear, he's likely to drift downward into an area where they are even less important and, in the end, this spiral hits bottom and he becomes a failure. I stirred this notion around in my mind and found myself thinking that competence could be a curse. A hard-working person could perform just well enough to hang on to a job for which he wasn't suited. His real talents might never be used; he might never even know that he had them. You had to dig to succeed, but, as Phil said, it helped if you dug where there was gold.

No, I'd give it a few weeks yet. That sort of job would always be around. In the meantime, something *had* to click.

In mid-October, it happened.

It came out of the blue while I was still working my way through the interviews which I had lined up with my second flight of letters. Janet met me at the door one evening with an envelope in her hand and the return address made me catch my breath.

"It's probably an ad," I said, but it wasn't. It was a letter signed by an executive vice-president who "understood that you might be available" for an opening "which has been created in our organization." I put it on the living room table and took off my coat and hat and poured myself a drink and read it again. "Hey," I said. "Hey, boy. Things are beginning to move."

"Take it easy," said Janet, "you haven't got the job yet."

"The hell with that," I told her. "Things are beginning to move. You get bids from outfits like this and things are rolling." The phone booth and the budget suddenly seemed very remote. I might have been locked out for a few chilly minutes but the door was opening now and everything was going to be okay. They were my sort of people, I could feel that. Somebody else might get this particular spot, but they'd be blind if they simply let me walk out the door. Good executives, tailor-made for your own organization, were too hard to find.

It took a tremendous amount of self-control to walk past my phone booth the next morning, but I made myself do it; I wasn't going to commit the basic blunder of overeagerness. I had an appointment that morning with a small but solid agency which was looking for a good man to fill a good job at a good, if not exciting salary. One day before I might have been interested; now I had a yardstick in my mind and I was measuring everything they said against it. It sounded attractive, but not quite attractive enough, not for a man with a bid from the big time in his pocket. In the end, I said I wanted to think it over.

I forced myself to have a leisurely lunch at Philippe's, where I was welcomed with the old time unctuousness. Philippe evidently had the ability to read letters in inside pockets. The check was steep but I paid it cheerfully, sternly suppressing the thought that it represented a couple of days' commuting fare. At 2:30 I left the restaurant and strolled over to Grand Central. Please God, I thought, let the call go right through so I don't have to ding-ding a dime in the middle of a chat with their executive vice-president.

It took me less than two minutes, however, to set up a date with the affable man at the other end of the line for ten o'clock the following morning. I gathered my change and patted the telephone, feeling almost an affection for it. When I got settled I was going to come back and make a couple of calls from that booth, just to see what it felt like. I played with the idea of calling Janet and telling her I was heading straight home; then I decided to stick to my rule and take the regular commuter train. You never knew. I killed some time at the newsreel theater in the station, sauntered along Madison Avenue and wound up back at Grand Central shortly before train time. It was a good ride and Westchester never looked better as it oozed past the windows. Things were on the up-bounce.

There was a blazing, pointless row with Janet after dinner that night while I was packing my attaché case for the next day. "Hadn't you better take your scrapbook?" she asked and I went through the roof. "What the hell do you think this is?" I asked. "Some kid peddling his clips from the college literary magazine?" More squabbling started when we checked over my résumé. Poise, assurance, integrity; that's what these people stood for and that's what they'd want to see on any piece of paper I handed them. She was for some items, I was against them, but with a change here and there, we achieved a simple, straightforward professional biography. Janet typed it up and I poured myself a drink and apologized to her. "I'm just nervous," I explained and she said, "Okay, get it out of your system now."

This was normal. I always felt jumpy when I was setting things up for a tough one; I wanted to be sure the plans were complete and nothing was being left out. I felt calm enough the next morning, standing in front of their building. It was a huge glass block, one of a row of immense paperweights pinning down the heart of Manhattan. "Well," I said. "Here we go."

Everyone smiled; that was the first thing I noticed. The receptionist smiled as I stepped off the elevator and the secretary smiled when she came out to the lobby to show me the way in and her boss came out from behind his desk with a smile and his hand extended as I walked into his office.

"I'm awfully sorry," he said. "Your appointment was with Bill but he had to run out to one of the plants today. Perhaps you won't mind talking with me?"

He began with a few routine questions. I had a hunch that this interview was a screening; I was getting a quick once-over before Bill spent his valuable time on me. I didn't wear a beard or sandals, so they could check one item off the list. I hadn't made a pass at the secretary, so they could eliminate another. My host settled back in his chair to work his way gracefully, if somewhat ponderously, through the rest of the specifications.

This didn't mean I could be careless; it simply meant that my answers were less important than the manner in which I gave them. It was the total impression that counted and the hard-core interviewing would come later. I sketched my background with a light touch—confidence without arrogance was the keynote here —but I was waiting for one particular question. It was his last question and he backed into it smoothly enough. "Your work sounds fascinating," he said. "I should think you would have hated to leave it."

"I did. I hated to leave the work and I hated to leave the people. But, after all, I had to think of the future."

There was a long silence. He was waiting for me to enlarge on this misty sentiment and I had no intention of doing so. As Phil had said, if you left when you didn't want to leave you were bounced, and if someone asks why you were bounced there isn't any good answer. There may be a good explanation, but there isn't any good answer.

So I simply waited and he finally picked up the ball.

|40|

"And you didn't feel that there was a good future where you were?"

"There was an excellent one. But for the past few years or so I felt I was developing along lines which could be put to fuller use in an organization such as yours." This was a mirror image of the truth, since I had developed along lines which were being put to less and less use in the agency.

"A good many agency people move over to the corporate side for similar reasons," I added, and immediately kicked myself. This was an unnecessary reminder and it came close to the edge of too much explanation. He stared at his blotter for a moment, and apparently decided not to press the point.

"Well," he said, "I won't take any more of your time. We'll give you some material to look over so you can get some idea of our operations and possibly some of our problems. Bill can see you at about three, tomorrow afternoon, if that's suitable?" This was my passing grade.

I smiled at the secretary and the receptionist as I left.

That night I hurried through supper and then settled down with the stuff I had brought home. By midnight I was wildly enthusiastic.

"Look at this!" I said to Janet. "No, wait a minute, let me skip through it and read you some stuff."

I leafed through the sheets, picking out a sentence here and a paragraph there. It all added up to the fact that fresh ideas geared to careful planning was the keynote of their operation. Once a project was launched, it was essential that every part of it keep pace. "That's it!" I said. "It's not enough to get things done—that's the point I've always hammered on. They've got to fit together." I'd had a hunch that this was my company; now I knew it. Status, security, salary; these were obvious attractions but there was an even bigger one: I could do something for them.

Bill's impressive title was worn by a small, balding man with a habit of taking off his horn-rimmed spectacles when he looked at someone and then putting them back on again when he wanted to read.

"I wonder," he said, "if you happen to have a résumé?"

I produced my brief biography and he put on his spectacles and

|41|

glanced at it. "Ah, yes," he said, "I just wanted to refresh my memory. Now we can talk." It was probable that most of the information had already been passed on to him, so he must have asked for the résumé mainly to see how I went about describing myself on paper. He steered me into a conversation about my marketing experience, nodding from time to time, or tossing out occasional questions: "Why did you do it that way?" or "What would you have done if that space *hadn't* been available?"

In the last half an hour or so he nudged the talk away from business and into the personal area. His questions were casual, but they probed a bit deeper than I liked. By the time this gentle pumping had ended, he knew where my father had been educated and what he had done for a living, where my wife had been born and brought up and how much education she had and where our kids went to school and what sort of house we lived in. He probably could have made a pretty shrewd guess, in fact, at how much we had paid for it.

"The suburbs," he remarked. "They offer so much and yet it never seems to be quite enough, at least for the women. My wife finds she has to make a couple of shopping trips to the city every week. I expect yours does, too."

Janet didn't—she was usually too busy—but I said yes, she did. I could see what was coming.

"I was going to suggest that you have lunch with me and a couple of the boys early next week," he said. "Tuesday, perhaps, if that's all right with you. Perhaps if that's one of her days to come in, your wife might enjoy joining us."

And that was it for the day. He walked out to the elevators with me, stopping at his secretary's desk so she could make a note of the lunch date. "By the way," he said, "I almost forgot. You don't mind running through some of our standard tests, do you? If you happen to be in town Monday you might drop in on our personnel department and get that over with. I'll tell them to expect you. It's just routine." He smiled at me as the elevator doors closed.

"Oh, Christ," said Janet when I told her about the lunch, but I wasn't worried about that. She knew the drill and would be the perfect corporate wife. "Of course, you realize," she added, "that I will have to go in Monday to get my hair done and buy some things." She felt better when she'd actually made the trip and was back home, revolving in front of the mirror to survey the effect of new hair styling, new shoes, a new purse and a new hat. I winced when I saw the bill but I didn't say anything. It was an investment.

I spent part of the weekend cramming for the tests and most of Monday taking them. There are several books about testing and I studied a couple of them, put this information together with what I had been told by friends, and got the general picture. The basic trick was to figure out what sort of man the company wanted and slant your answers in that direction, making sure you weren't caught in any inconsistencies. You shouldn't claim an interest in both boxing and poetry because the basic American credo holds that they never go together. One of the toughest guys I ever met was an armored force sergeant who loved barroom brawls and Browning with equal enthusiasm, but one of the keys to taking these tests was to accept the tester's world.

The smiling apparently stopped someplace south of the personnel director and his aides, who told me I was being "processed." There was an application form; I glanced at it and said I'd mail it in after I'd looked up some of the dates. I wanted a chance to study the form before filling it in. Some of the questions were pretty personal and I didn't like the idea of the answers lying around in a filing cabinet where a good many people might have access to them. It also occurred to me that this form would be a handy thing for the company to have if I ever landed a responsible position with one of their competitors.

The written test was one of the standard types. I ran my eye over it to catch the general drift; then made a mental note of the answers which would add up to the image of a conservative, fairly uncomplicated but reasonably ambitious man. The testers irritated me. These people had no authority to hire me and yet they could prevent me from being hired. They could rule on my suitability for an advertising job, though they knew nothing about advertising or the attitudes which were suitable for it.

The application form irked me, too, as I worked my way through it that night. It was pretty exhaustive: what sort of activities had I joined in school? I listed the sports and class offices but omitted the school literary magazine. Military service: what rank?

|43|

I put down "sergeant," conscious of the fact that it should have been "captain." For the first time in my life, I was apologizing for my Army record.

We were back on smiling ground again during the lunch on Tuesday. There was a difference, apparently, between their paper left hand and their personal right. Janet handled her end with practiced smoothness; she was neither too eager nor too offhand when Bill coaxed out hints as to her attitude toward the demands of a corporate career. We were all good friends when the lunch ended and Bill suggested that I drop in Wednesday morning, "10-ish or so," to have a look around and "meet some more of the boys." Janet and I caught an early train home and we stuck discreetly to small talk during the ride; on a suburban train you can never be sure who's sitting in the seat in front of you. In the privacy of our own car, however, I asked her how the set-up had struck her.

"It's all right, I guess," she said. "I've got a feeling these are the type of people who have to be invited to the house at regular intervals and that means some redecorating."

"It can't be helped. That's part of the game."

"I know," she said wearily. "Maybe someday, when we retire, we can have a home. You know, a place where the people you invite are guests and behave themselves as guests or they don't get asked again."

"You have to be very rich or very poor to live like that. If you're in-between, you just have to play along with the system. After all," I added, "we've done pretty well out of it; we've got a nice home and we can afford a good many luxuries."

"Sometimes I wonder about that word 'luxury.' Is it always something you buy, or is privacy a luxury, too?"

"Privacy is something you buy," I answered, "And right now we can't afford it."

"Okay, okay," she said. "I'm playing along."

I reported to Bill's office at 10:05 the following morning—my interpretation of "10-ish"—and was taken on a guided tour of the offices and then to the executive dining room for lunch with the marketing director. I went home with another batch of printed material which included the founder's biography. Surprisingly, this turned out to be rather fascinating. I dug into it on the train and found myself caught up in a revolution, sparked by an impatient individualist who had up-ended the stuffed shirts of his time and backed the cranks who were bringing new ideas into the world.

I couldn't help wondering one thing: how would he have made out in those tests?

Saturday morning I wrote a note to the small agency, saying thanks, but I wasn't available. Then I drove Cliff down to the shore to look at boats. I knew less about them than I should and I wanted to shop around before making a final decision. Marge and Melly turned up Saturday evening, all set for a hot game of bridge. "Bridge, hell," I said. "Let's run up to the country club and have dinner."

"Are you *sure* you aren't too tired?" asked Janet in a voice heavy with significance.

"Oh, cut it out," I said. "I think we've got something to celebrate and we're going to celebrate." After that remark, of course, I had to spell out the whole story. Margie clapped her hands and squealed, "Gee, that's terrific" and Melly said they were a sound organization, very sound. Three drinks and a dinner later, at the country club, it occurred to him to ask when I started.

"It isn't settled yet," I answered, "but don't worry about it."

"I hope you aren't celebrating prematurely," said the skeleton at my feast.

I was beginning to feel the liquor; I hadn't been doing much drinking through the previous weeks. "Melly," I said, "you always seem to be happiest when you're prophesying doom. So it does fall through; I'm rolling, that's the point. If I can get something going with these boys, I can get something going someplace else just as easily." The waiter brought us another round and I raised my glass. "A toast," I said, "to the new career."

NOVEMBER

"You Pay Cash from Now On"

They vanished like a magician's rabbit.

It took me a couple of weeks to realize what had happened. I hung around the house through the first week waiting for a call. Monday was a long day, Tuesday was longer, Wednesday I found myself itching to pick up the phone and talk to Bill.

"You'll melt the damn thing if you keep staring at it," said Janet. "Why don't you take the afternoon off before we both go nuts?" I made her promise to camp by the phone like a debutante before the prom, then I drove Cliff down to another boatyard. Sail areas and Fiberglas hulls; "a fine boat, sir, very easy for a boy to handle." A sudden hunch hit me that Bill's office was on the line to the house. I'd been a fool to go out; Wednesday was the logical day for them to call. I looked at my watch and calmed down. We could finish our visit and still get home in time to return the call— if there had been one.

We pulled into the driveway before five. I was calm as hell. I drove the car into the garage and closed the garage doors and picked up a couple of scraps of paper in the yard before I strolled into the house. Janet was in the living room, reading a magazine. She looked up and shook her head.

I took off my jacket and sat down. So much for hunches.

"I've been right here the whole time," Janet said. "I haven't left the room for a moment, except to go into the kitchen. If anyone had called I would have heard them."

"I know that," I said. "I was just wondering if the phone was okay."

"Well, Margie phoned, so we're getting incoming calls. And I phoned the butcher. I want to talk to you about that, by the way, when you have the time."

Thursday afternoon I broke down and tried to reach Bill.

"Do you think it's wise?" Janet asked. I told her I did; they must have mailed a letter which went astray or tried to get through by phone and failed. "There must have been *something,*" I said. "Even if they've changed signals there'd be something. I'd get one of those 'application for employment' notes at the very least."

Bill was tied up in a conference. "It will be an all-day meeting," his secretary added helpfully, so I said okay, I'd try him Friday morning and she said he would be out of town Friday. I left a message that I'd called.

I half expected something in the mail Friday morning, but there were only a couple of bills and an ad. Friday afternoon, I drafted a note:

Dear Bill:

I'm sorry if you've been trying to reach me and couldn't. I was called out of town Monday and didn't get back until noon on Thursday.

Just wanted to let you know I've cleaned up my business and should be available through most of next week.

Best regards.

I stayed intensely available, puttering around the house, watching television, helping Janet with small chores.

"What was that mystery story?" I asked her one day. "The one about the trial?" There had been something in it about the jury being out for a long time. This was a good omen for the defendant or a bad one; I couldn't recall which and neither could Janet. At any rate, there would be an answer to my note, if nothing else, by Friday.

There wasn't.

|47|

I tried Bill again. He was out.

I tried Bill's assistant. He was tied up.

Friday was an Indian summer day, mild and bright. I poured myself a drink and went out to the patio, where I sat in the sunlight and swallowed a few simple facts:

I had wanted that job, and not merely to get in off the street. I had wanted it because it was my job; I had wanted it because they were my sort of people. If I hadn't wanted it so very much, what was clear to me now would have been clear to me ten days before: they weren't going to hire me and that letter of regret would arrive as soon as some secretary got around to typing it.

"Never mind, things are moving," I said out loud, trying to recapture that mood. It didn't help. Perhaps the last afternoon of an empty week was the wrong time to try it. Monday morning would be better and Monday morning I would head for the city again.

I wandered back in the house and looked at the phone, black and stolid on the table. It was a wonderful invention if the right person were on the other end, but then so was the Pony Express. Janet came into the room and I said, "I'm going into town Monday."

"Do you want me to stay in all day, then?"

"The hell with it," I answered. "The only thing I'm going to get from them now is a letter, and that'll wait."

Saturday wasn't much fun. Cliff wanted to reach some decision on the boat and I fended him off. Marge and Melly came over and Melly's sixth sense began to click like a Geiger counter. "Looks like it's fallen through," he said, and I agreed that it certainly seemed to have fallen through and how about some bridge? "I thought you were counting your chickens before they were hatched," he added and, after fifteen years of co-existence, I found myself seriously weighing the idea of socking my brother-in-law in the chops.

I spent Sunday brooding.

I had made the job hunter's classic mistake; I had tried to juggle two spots and I had lost both. Well, what do you do? You can't take Job A and then quit it a week later if Job B comes through.

I was to learn later that you certainly can. This came from a salesman I met who had joined one firm and paid his first "sales calls" each day on two others which were still thinking about him. "You can't be squeamish about this," he told me. "For them it's just an inconvenience; for you and your wife and kids it's survival. Besides, those other spots won't come through. I know some of those boys like a book. Half the time they haven't even got a genuine opening. They're just window-shopping for personnel. They like to keep a stream of guys flowing through on the off-chance some genius will wander in."

Thus the philosophy of one seasoned job hunter.

I had lost nearly a month in time. I had lost more than a month in money and the thought of Janet's new clothes and those dinners at the country club made me shiver. I had to get caught up, and quickly. The first step must be taken at home and it wasn't going to be easy. "We're going to have to go back to the budget," I told Janet, "and this time we're going to have to pinch every damn penny."

"The kids, too?" she asked.

"The kids, too. The boat, the country club, the works. You can just forget the date on the calendar; from now on this is 1932. We turn off lights when we aren't using them and we close the doors upstairs to save heat and we buy things where they're two cents cheaper." I went on like this for some time and I felt pretty lousy about it because it was Janet who had tried to slow me down when I was staging celebrations and it was Janet who was going to have to carry the load. We had to do it, though. Those nickels and dimes bought time and we had to buy back a whole month.

Janet raised two major points:

"We could get rid of one of the cars," she suggested. "The small one's cheaper to run. We could get a chunk of cash for the other and we'd save."

"Maybe we should hang on to the big one. We'll be getting a new car someday—at least I hope we will—and it's got a much better trade-in value."

"The trade-in's someday," she pointed out, "we need the cash now."

I agreed, bitterly, that this made sense. The big car would have to go.

Janet's second suggestion was that she find a job.

"I could get something right in town. A part-time job, perhaps, while the boys are in school. It wouldn't bring in much but every little bit helps."

"What sort of job?"

"I don't know; I'd have to see what there was. One of the stores, or some office which needed a part-time secretary."

I wasn't crazy about the idea. If Janet started work in some local store our position would be as conspicuous as hell; it would amount to an advertisement that I couldn't support my family.

Well, let's face it, I couldn't.

"Why don't I have a look around?" she added. "There's no point in arguing about it until I know whether I could get one."

We left it at that.

One evening I found out how tough the budget problem really was. Sorting some papers, I turned up the butcher's bill. "Wasn't there something about this?" I asked, holding it up.

"It's all right. It's been cleared up."

She said it a bit too quickly and I swung around and looked at her.

"Okay, so it's been cleared up. I wanted to know what there was to clear up."

"I wasn't going to tell you, not with all that going on and everything. But I thought the bill was a little bit too high. There were a couple of things on it I couldn't remember ever getting. I called him up and asked him to double-check it. I said we wouldn't pay it until he did. *He* said . . ."

"Well?"

"*He* said we'd better pay. He said he'd yank us into small claims court so fast it wouldn't be funny, if we didn't." She drew a deep breath. "He said—just like this—'I ain't carrying any deadbeats and you better get that straight. You pay that bill today and you pay cash from now on.' And then he hung up."

"And you paid it?"

"It was only a couple of dollars over," Janet answered dully. "And small claims court . . . He'd have done it, you know."

"I'm going to see him in the morning," I said. "I'm going to drop by on my way to the station and I'm going to have a little talk with that lad. When I get through with him he isn't going to insult my wife or anybody's wife, ever again."

|50|

"It won't do any good to argue with him."

"I'm not going to argue with him. I'm going to belt him in that smart mouth of his."

"You're getting all worked up," she said. "That won't do any good and neither will getting yourself arrested for assault."

"Okay, okay. But stay away from him. If he doesn't want our business we won't force it on him."

"I can't," Janet protested, "not if we're going to cut down on the car expenses. Where else can I go?"

"I'll carry meat out from the city every day if I have to, or we'll go without it altogether. He isn't getting any more of our business, now or ever. Just as long as we've got one dollar left that dollar's as good as anyone else's."

"You're getting all worked up again," said Janet.

"I'm getting pretty sick of being pushed around by butchers, I can tell you that. And by everyone else." I stood up and headed for the kitchen, but I stopped at the door. "As far as that goes there's just a certain amount of courtesy one human being owes to another, whether they're big customers or small customers or cash customers or what the hell. This butcher is not only a lousy butcher but he's a slob, too. Personally, I mean, he's a stinking slob."

"I don't want to shop there," said Janet. "I'm just trying to save money. If you think it's such a ball, you just come along. That's all I'm asking, you just come with me and see how you like it."

"It's my fault you're treated like dirt—that's what you're saying isn't it?"

"That *isn't* what I said." We were both edgy and I knew it, but I couldn't stop myself.

"It's what you meant, all right. And I just feel damn sorry for you, that's all. The only people you know are people whose courtesy has to be bought and now we're too broke to buy any."

"Is that your third drink?" Janet asked. "Or just your second?"

I ignored her question. "You can quit worrying," I continued. "I'll get something, sooner or later, and then you can go buy back their friendship. I'll get an affidavit that I'm employed and you can take it around to them and get your membership card back."

This seemed like a good exit line and I marched out to the kitchen. It wasn't much of a fight; we'd had worse ones. It did happen to be the first fight touched off by the tensions of unemployment and that bothered me. I wondered what would happen when the squeeze really went on.

The Sunday papers were strewn around the kitchen and I leafed through them, killing time to give Janet a chance to cool off. They were pregnant with advertising. Here was a diamond pin, a "fanciful trifle" at three hundred and fifty dollars; here again an ordinary soft drink at a dime a bottle, meant for "today's smart young moderns." Sapphires or cigarettes, diamonds or detergent, a note of snobbishness ran through much of the copy and I could see where the butcher got his ideas. One hair tonic ad bit especially deep. "The symbols of success," it began. "His sleek sports car, his imported wines, his apartment at an 'in' address . . ."

I knew the rest of that purple prose by heart. I had okayed the layout myself.

"Well," I said aloud. "I suppose a nation gets the shopkeepers it deserves." For some reason, probably because of the drinks, this struck me as an exceptionally brilliant epigram and I went back in the living room to apologize to Janet and repeat it to her. And for some reason, possibly because of the argument, she was willing to see it as brilliant, too.

That evening Max Weltchek dropped in.

"I was driving by," he explained, settling his bear-like bulk into an easy chair, "and it occurred to me that if I got home too early I might have to do something useful around the house. I will loaf here for a while, if I may; I have been doing useful things all afternoon." He had been down at the fishing docks, supervising the installation of some equipment on a boat.

"On Sunday?" I asked, and Max grinned.

"I don't keep office hours, not if I want to hang on to their business."

"Are they big spenders, then?" The butcher was still on my mind.

"Big spenders?" Max repeated. "I get a bigger markup on one set of monogrammed cocktail glasses for the yacht club crowd. No, they're not big spenders, but they're steady. My old man used to call them 'the rent payers.' "

"I don't get it," I said.

"That's the way the old man used to break it down. The fishermen and the workmen who bought tools—they were 'the rent-payers.' As long as you had them, in good times or bad, you'd always be able to pay your rent. The people who came in and bought fancy plumbing—it was fancy plumbing in those days rather than boats and carriage lamps—they were the profit customers. Any smart businessman pays his rent before he starts spending his profits. The old man took care of the customers who paid his overhead before the customers who represented his profit. He'd spend half an hour finding a set of fittings, even if he only made a nickel on them."

"Too many of those five-cent half hours could put a man out of business these days," I objected.

"Sure they could," Max agreed, "if you run that sort of place. Me, I skim what I can off the top of the carriage lamp crowd, but I'm not what they call geared to the times—these times or any other. Call it an investment, if you like, or a part of my overhead, but if times change, I want to be able to change with them. My old man, now; he may have moved kind of slow during the Twenties, but he stayed in business during the depression."

"Then you think there's going to be a depression?"

Max shook his head. "I didn't say that," he answered. "I said times would change; they always have and they always will. The firms which survive—the *people* who survive—are the ones with something basic they can carry over. People will always buy hardware, but not always the same items. If I'd been trained to sell carriage lamps, I'd go out of business when they went out of fashion."

I went to bed early that Sunday; there was a good deal to do the next day. Just before I fell asleep I remembered one thing which hadn't been done that weekend and would have to be done soon: sometime within the next few days, Cliff would have to be told that he wasn't going to get his boat.

Monday and Tuesday were tiring days and wasted ones. I dropped in on a couple of people, but I stayed away from the phone booth. I couldn't face it yet.

I was still waiting for some final word from good old Bill and his gang. As the time slid by and no letter arrived a suspicion touched the edge of my mind, like a sound half-heard in the night. Phil was one of the few people I could talk to candidly, and I told him about it over a lunch.

"Look at the pattern," I said. "They're definitely interested and we're really talking business. And then—wham—they just disappear. Now what does that mean?"

"It means you got turned down," answered Phil. "I'm damn sorry; I know how much you wanted that spot. But people have been turned down before."

I wasn't getting my point across. "That's just it," I said, leaning across the table. "I did *not* get turned down; I got dropped like a hot brick. They don't want me for any job, now or ever. I'm not even worth a form letter which says, 'Sorry, the spot's been filled.' I'm a . . . a . . . responsible guy, Phil; I've got some little standing in my profession. No, I think the whole business adds up to something."

"Like what?"

"Like somebody spreading some story which would make that sort of outfit drop me; something that would put me beyond the pale as far as they're concerned."

"Oh, for Christ's sake," said Phil, leaning back in his chair and looking directly at me. "I thought you were the smart ad guy. Haven't you ever seen a brush-off before?"

"Sure I have, I've seen lots of them. But this crew is so image-conscious that they gold-plate their garbage cans. They've got a public relations budget bigger than the national debt. And you think they're going to make an enemy of a guy who still knows plenty of people in New York just to save a stamp and five minutes of a typist's time? I'll tell you what *would* make them do it and that's if they picked up some sort of story which convinced them they'd better get clear of any association with me and damn quick."

"*What* sort of story, for God's sake?"

"How do I know? It doesn't take much to hurt a guy in my position, you know that. Any hint, any rumor; firms like that are so nervous that any slight thing can do it. You can stab a guy even when you're pretending to praise him. Maybe the story isn't true, maybe you could prove it isn't; what good would that do you? You'd never get the chance. You could go on trying for jobs and getting turned down forever and never even know that was the reason."

"Question?" said Phil. "Who would want to do something like that to you?"

"Well, there again, how do I know? Some junior I once worked

|54|

with who's holding a grudge; some secretary. The way things are these days anybody could do it." That brought me to the question I had in the back of my mind. "Look, Phil," I added, "I wonder if you'd do something for me? I wonder if you'd give my old shop a call and say you're—oh, Mr. Bloggins of the Bloggins Machine Tool Company or something like that—and just ask them about me. This isn't an accusation or anything like that; I'm just curious. I'd like to see who the call gets routed to and what they say."

"No, I won't," said Phil bluntly. "One practical reason is that some of those people know me and they might recognize my voice. There's another reason, though: I'm not going to do anything to encourage this theory of yours." He leaned back in his chair again and lit a cigarette. "Now let me try to answer some of these points. First, your ernstwhile friends, for all their plush-lined toilet seats, do boot one sometimes. If they didn't, they wouldn't need a whole army of professional image merchants to keep bailing them out. Second, some public relations is like the paint on a cheap product; it's slapped on thick where it shows but not where it doesn't. It only extends downward to a certain level and they figured—don't get sore now—that you were below that level. Finally, I've been expecting this. I haven't been in your position, thank God, but I've seen guys that have and I may know a bit more about it than you do. You're feeling pretty sensitive and this 'somebody's spreading a story about me' is a standard reaction at this stage."

"What the hell are you?" I asked bitterly. "Some sort of curbstone psychiatrist?"

"No, I'm a salesman. I get around to a lot of companies and I get a chance to measure one against another. I meet a lot of people and some of them don't bother to put on their cocktail party face, not for a salesman. I'll admit I may even encourage this a bit with my non-status symbol." The big, battered briefcase was under the table as usual and he gave it a kick. "It's useful, sometimes, to know which guys attach more importance to the outside of a briefcase than the inside.

"I wonder how many bastards you've really met in your lifetime," he continued. "I don't mean people who try to climb over you in office politics; I mean guys who kick the cat when they think nobody's looking. You see, you happen to be something you've never been before; you're vulnerable."

"Now wait a minute . . ." I began, but Phil held up his hand.

|55|

"You're vulnerable," he insisted. "You can be hurt. There's a type of guy who senses that you can be hurt and he ... kicks the cat. As for your late chums, they're the back-to-the-womb boys. You remember that line about 'windows in the soul?' Well, they have mirrors. The rest of the world, and the people in it, just don't exist for them. If someone has troubles or they don't like him or he isn't their type—pfft—there isn't any such person."

I noticed with some surprise that Phil was getting angry. His face was pink. "The guy who kicks people and the guy who pretends not to notice," he said. "In some circles they're just normal people, but take away a little bit of restraint and you see them the way I do. Take away a little bit more and you see them the way you're learning to. Take away a bit more and you see them the way a lot of helpless people did in Europe a few years ago. You don't think people can be this way so you put it in the only framework you know—office politics." He shook his head. "Nobody's spreading any story about you; you're just running into a certain type of person and you'd better be ready for plenty more of them."

The waiter brought the check and Phil took it with an authoritative hand. "It works the other way, too," he added. "If you're vulnerable, it brings out the human being in a lot of people. You may meet nicer guys than you've ever met before."

"Who's in control?" I asked. "The sick ones or the human beings?"

"If I knew that," said Phil, dragging his briefcase from under the table, "I could tell you how you're going to end up. And I'm going to end up. And the whole star-spangled country's going to end up."

DECEMBER

"There's Always More Where We Came From"

Few works of fiction could have been more eloquent than my bankbook. It told me, quite clearly, that if I had said yes to the offers I "couldn't afford" to take in July, we would have been much better off now, in December. Oddly, I had no regrets; it still seemed wise to turn down an unsuitable spot when I could. From this point on, I couldn't. Like some grim, step-by-step set of instructions for the unemployed, the bankbook said I could no longer set my sights high.

It took me four more weeks to discover that I couldn't set them low, either.

I went back to the phone booth where I was depressed by the sight of two numbers I had scribbled on the wall more than a month before. The best person to call, perhaps, was Sid, but the memory of my parting comment at that lunch—"obviously I can do better"—was too embarrassing. I put him at the bottom of the list and began with the other ad agencies which had offered me jobs.

The first one: "Sorry, we *did* have that opening, of course, but that was several months ago . . ."

The second one: Mr. Whatzit was in conference all day. He would be out of town tomorrow. And the next day, too.

The Job Hunter: The Diary
of a "Lost" Year

The companies came next. I drew a blank with the first one and a weak nibble from the second: "Well, yes, we *did* have some idea . . . but our circumstances have changed a good deal since then. Just a minute . . ." Some sort of hurried consultation evidently took place at the other end. "I think you might drop by, if you have a moment. I can't promise anything, of course. We could have a talk, but . . ."

"Sure," I said. "Fine. Thank you." I stepped out of the phone booth and began to wander, block after aimless block, walking to nowhere and feeling more frightened than I ever had before in my life. There are fears beyond the things you fear and fears beyond them, too, one circle below another, and on that cold, clear day in the heart of midtown Manhattan I was close to panic.

At one time, a thousand years before, I had been afraid of a possible setback. Then I had found the sharp-edged fear of failure; the fear that I had drawn my bow and missed and must drudge my way to the grave. I had hoped for a good job; I had been prepared for a fair one; I had feared being forced into a poor one. It had never occurred to me that I might not be able to find a job—any job—at all.

You there, my friend—yes, you, with the attaché case and the gray Homburg, what can you turn your hand to? Vice-president and division manager? Good for you, but suppose the market is a bit tight for vice-presidents and division managers this year? Well, one thing's certain, you won't actually starve. There are a lot of lesser jobs you could handle. A man who has sold million-dollar deals could certainly sell neckties; a man who has run three factories could run one gas station. You could punch an adding machine, drive a taxi; you're still in good physical shape, you could dig ditches. You could get by somehow. Or could you?

No, my friend, stick to your last if you can. When people want neckties sold, they hire necktie salesmen. They ask the questions they were asking about me: What's wrong with him? Why is he willing to take such an enormous cut? Business is booming, why can't he find a job at his own level? We don't want any drunks or nuts in here; we don't want any incompetents or has-beens. We don't want some top-brass drop-out using our store as a life-boat until he's picked up by a corporation.

If he's good, we won't keep him; if he isn't, we don't want him.

The walking tired me and the fatigue dulled my fears. There were, after all, several avenues I hadn't explored. One thing I had not done, for example, was to seek professional help.

With this on my mind, I made my first approach to an "executive employment agency" where I was interviewed by a brisk, glib little woman. Her analysis: "You've got a problem, doll." This was a conclusion I had already reached myself; if I hadn't had a problem, I pointed out to her, I wouldn't need an employment agency. She shrugged and handed me a form. "Fill it out," she said, "and we'll see what we can do." I never heard from them again.

A second agency refused to set an appointment by phone. "Just write a letter, please," said an impersonal male voice. "Enclose two copies of a résumé. Please do not telephone; we will get in touch with you." They never did.

The third attempt brought me face to face with a bored middle-aged man. "You are not . . . ah . . . currently employed?" he asked, and I confessed I wasn't. "That makes it difficult," he said, "very difficult. Now, if you *were* currently employed . . ." This time I was the one who shrugged.

Push, push, hammer, hammer, try to get people moving. I stalked out to the corridor, feeling angry, and glared at a neatly tailored man who was waiting for the elevator. I was going to sort him out if he was one of the employment agency people, but he wasn't. He was merely another job hunter. "Nine months now," he announced without embarrassment. "That ought to be a good gestation period for a job."

"Are they all like that?" I asked, jerking my head toward the outer door of the office.

"Some are, some aren't." He glanced at his watch. "Why don't you have lunch with me, if you have nothing else to do, and I'll fill you in as much as I can. There's an Automat just around the corner."

The only empty table we could find was by the window. As we unloaded our trays, I studied this man who had been battering on closed doors almost twice as long as myself. He seemed alert and even cheerful, but there were small tip-offs: the tight lines at the corners of his mouth, the eyes which were grim even when he smiled, the sardonic edge to his voice.

"My name is Leslie—Les," he said. "I gather you're a new member of the club."

I didn't like that phrase "the club"; it seemed to lump me with every has-been who haunted employment agencies hoping for a break. "Things are a bit slow," I said, "and I've been taking the opportunity to look over the field. I . . ."

"How long have you been out?" he asked bluntly.

"Well, we took a month's vacation—a little more, actually, and we . . ."

"How long?"

I gave in. "Five months," I admitted.

"Five months." He held up one hand, the fingers spread. "First month, you took your vacation. What was it, really? Two weeks?"

"Oh, all right, it was three."

"Three weeks. And then the second month—and the third, maybe—were spent chasing around among people you already knew and projects which were supposed to be in the works?" I nodded and he ticked off the next point. "The fourth month you began to get organized and fire out some letters on a planned basis, and someplace along the line you lost a couple of weeks to a deal which was all set?"

"More than that," I said. "It was a month."

He whistled softly. "You were unlucky. I spotted what was happening in a couple of weeks. Still, I shot two weeks' worth of cash on a trip which turned out to be a false alarm, so we're about even. Watch those out-of-town deals—they can be murder."

He opened his briefcase and took out a small notebook. "Let me give you the names of some executive agencies," he said, ripping out a blank page. "These are the ones I've had pretty good luck with so far." He scribbled for a few moments while I pondered the implications of those two words, "good luck." However good these agencies were, they obviously hadn't found Les a job.

"Try some of these," he suggested, handing the list across the table. He must have sensed my thought because he added: "They can't *get* you a job, you know; they can only point you at one. But these outfits are good, they'll work with you. As for the others—well, I guess there are a lot of problems in their business."

"I don't want to hear about their problems," I said bitterly. "I'm paying them to help me solve mine."

"There's Always More
Where We Came From"

My companion shrugged—it was a gesture which seemed to go with employment agencies. "Let's face it," he said. "There's always more where we came from."

He told me his own story. From a youngster just out of the Air Force in 1946, he had worked his way up to branch office manager for an appliance firm. It was a good job, but he had ambitions which went much further. "It makes me laugh now," he said, "to think of the plans I had. I used to spend my evenings and my weekends working on expansion projects. What I didn't know was that they were obsolete before I even got them down on paper, and so was I. The firm was heading in a new direction all right, but they weren't taking me along."

One day a kid with a vague title—"coordinator" of something or other—reported for work from New York and calmly set up his own system of correspondence with the front office. The management evidently knew all about it and within a few weeks the kid was running the place. He had to: he was the one who got the directives from headquarters and he wasn't disposed to pass them on. Les struggled on for several months and finally handed in his resignation.

"If I'd known what it was like," he said, "I'd have stuck there and drawn my pay check, even if I'd had to sweep out the office." He rummaged in his pockets, pulled out a crumpled cigarette and lit it in defiance of the NO SMOKING sign which hung just over our heads. "Or maybe I wouldn't have stuck," he added. "Maybe we all have to go through this, and the sooner we get it over with, the better."

"You talk as if it were inevitable," I said.

"For a lot of people, I think it is." He paused for a moment and studied the burning end of his cigarette. "When I first got shoved out I thought all I had lost was a job. That's no fun in itself, if you've spent a lot of years working your way up to it, but it isn't a patch on losing a career. I wandered around in a daze for about four months or so before I realized I'd been hit by something a lot bigger than a shake-up in one firm."

"Like what?" I asked.

"Who knows? Everyone's got his own idea. I think it's like very thin ice on a very deep lake. The lucky ones never break through. But if you do, you don't drop just a couple of inches—you go down and down and down. *Somebody's* got to pay for the affluent society—it stands to reason—and from now on I guess that includes us. It's like—well, it's a sort of hidden depression. It's a great big pit outside everyone's office door. Maybe you don't put your foot into it, maybe you do." He stared through the window at the city: the buildings across the street and the taller buildings behind them and the other buildings, even taller, which served as a backdrop. "It drives you nuts," Les added.

"What does?"

"All those offices out there, thousands of them. In one of those offices right now they're knocking themselves out trying to find a guy with my qualifications. Maybe we can see it from here. But which one," he said, hammering softly on the table, "which one?"

The lunchtime crowd was beginning to pour in through the revolving doors. We pushed back our chairs and walked outside.

"Good luck," Les said, holding out his hand. "You try those agencies; I think you might get someplace with them. And another thing, if you don't mind some advice?"

"I can use anything," I said. "Go ahead."

"Don't keep to yourself. Find some of the other guys who are looking. You can trade information with them and that's useful. What's even better, you can trade experiences. It keeps you from stewing up funny ideas. You don't get to thinking it's all aimed at you personally, or maybe that there's something wrong with you."

I walked down Madison Avenue, not quite sure whether I should feel happy or grim. "A hidden depression." It was a discouraging thought and if my new friend was even partially right it meant some rough sledding ahead. At the same time, his warning against solitude made sense. The pain and the shame which I had bottled up within myself were not unique; other people had felt the sting of the same defeats.

That night I took out my "personal history" and studied it carefully. As the unhelpful woman had remarked, I had a problem, and yet, what was the problem? Presumably I was still an adman, if temporarily unaffiliated. All those years of experience, all those contacts, all those papers carried home on weekends—if I wasn't an adman, what was I? A man should have carved out his niche by the time he's forty, that's what they said. Well, I had carved my niche and now I couldn't find it.

"Advertising man"; what did the phrase mean? Copywriters were "advertising men"; illustrators were "advertising men"; salesmen, accountants, secretaries, receptionists and an entire, assorted gaggle of people who went under the loose title of "executive" were "advertising men" or women as the case might be. Was my lunchtime acquaintance an "appliance man?" Was Max Weltchek a "hardware man?" Was my beloved brother-in-law, apart from the other titles which an active imagination might find for him, a "stock market man?" If an accountant left an ad agency to look for a job, did he describe himself as "an advertising man" or as an accountant?

What was I, in terms of real skills and not job titles?

What had I actually done each day in the office?

"I'll tell you what," said Janet. "I'll get a pencil and paper and you just start talking, psychiatrist style. Every time you use a specialized word of any sort I'll yell 'jargon' and you back up and start over. Maybe we'll work something out that way."

"Okay," I answered. "Let's see, now. Money's always important, of course. I've had plenty of experience in handling it and that ought to interest anyone in any business. When you figure the time I spent on media buying . . ."

"Jargon!" said Janet.

It was tough going, but little by little we hammered it out. "Account solicitations" became "new business"; "client contacts" became "customer relations"; "budget" became "costs."

"Oh, come on!" I protested when Janet insisted on this last change. "Every business has budgets."

"Sure they do," she answered, "but do they use the word in the same sense that you do?" It was a good point and I made the substitution.

Slowly and painfully we worked our way down to bedrock. Recognizing and analyzing problems, that had been part of the job; finding and weighing possible solutions, planning, putting the plans into operation and following them up to make sure they operated smoothly. "And," I emphasized, "within the costs and time schedules which had been laid down. That ought to be the most important thing." I was beginning to get the feel of this digging down process. "After all," I told Janet, "any fool can build a bridge if he throws enough rocks into the river. You hire an engineer because he can build a much better bridge in a much shorter time for much less cost. That's what we want to say."

Once I had started this self-analysis, I found it difficult to stop. Had I liked being an adman for its own sake? Or had I really liked some element—call it X—which had found its best expression in the ad business but could be given some other job title?

I sat with my feet on the table and my eyes closed, reliving those years in a series of scenes. Copywriting: "Almost the right word won't do; there's *the* right one someplace." Clients: "He won't like it a year from now, but how do we make him see that now?" Budgets: "What we really need is more money, but let's see if we can do it with what we have." Faces, voices, failures, emergencies, victories. The dinner at which I had received my award: "A man with a green thumb for ad campaigns."

To see things grow; to fit the pieces together and watch something new take shape; to nurse it along, to fit one brick on top of another until you had a wall and then a shelter and finally a complete building with its own unique personality. People, problems, products, money; I could bring them together and build something from them and this is what I loved doing. There was no reason that I could see, no reason at all, why I couldn't do it in damn near any business.

The whole world was my hunting ground.

I told Janet this and while I was struggling to put my ideas into words, a thought struck me. "You know," I said, "this is the way industries lose people. I mean really lose them, for good."

"It doesn't bother them," she said, "so why should it bother you?"

I took the results of this soul-searching to two executive employment agencies on the list Les had given me and, as he had predicted, I found them both to be businesslike. Neither agency exactly oozed optimism; both had somewhat the air of a lawyer assigned to defend a client who had been caught with his hand in the cash register. Like good lawyers, however, they seemed determined to do their best and this cheered me up immensely. I was still confident of my ability to sell myself if I could reach the right person; perhaps these people would know where he was.

"I see you've taken the first step," said the interviewer in one agency, looking over my new résumé. "Still, you'll have to be prepared to go further than this. It isn't enough to avoid talking to people in your own terms—you've got to do your best to talk to them in their own." He had a story about a beer salesman who was turned down by a food packaging firm because "we want a food man." It was getting be a familiar story, he added; firms hired techniques rather than abilities. The applicant was a "beer man" to them, not a salesman. "You've made the transition," the interviewer said, tapping my résumé. "Now you're going to have to help them make it."

The second agency actually had a lead and sent me off to see the marketing director of a good-sized corporation. It was an odd sort of interview, and it ended with my confidence in my self-salesmanship badly shaken. The firm's offices and the marketing director himself were chillingly reminiscent of Bill and his building. Perhaps this got the interview off to a bad start, perhaps something else was wrong, I don't know. I did know, after the first few minutes, that it wasn't going very well.

He asked the usual questions with a friendly smile and I gave the right answers, except they weren't right, I could feel that. You don't plow through a hundred client presentations, as I had done, without developing a sixth sense which tells you when you aren't getting through. Ten minutes after I walked into his office the marketing director knew he didn't want to hire me. After that he was just a nice guy letting me down gently. I saw this and there wasn't a damn thing I could do about it.

This is just another client, I told myself. You know these people, you speak their language, you've stood up in front of them time after time and sold them something. Come on now, let's make a dent in this man.

But this man was standing up behind his desk and holding out his hand and saying thanks very much for dropping in, just turn left after you go through the doors and you shouldn't have any trouble finding the elevators.

I found myself out on the pavement, confused and a little bit frightened. Something about me had shouted "no" to the marketing manager just as surely as if I had slouched into his office and spit on the carpet. What, what, what?

I could think of nothing.

There was still my follow-up list and I plugged away at that without much hope. It had settled into a routine; I phoned the firms on the list once a week and asked if there were any developments, and they told me—sharply or cheerfully as the case might be—that there weren't. Jerry's outfit was still marinating its projects; Abbott and Costello still saw possibilities—very good possibilities—of an expansion in the future. I finally phoned Sid, who invited me out to lunch and filled an hour with small talk. In the end I asked him point-blank if there were still any possibility of joining his agency at the salary he and Abe had offered, and he simply looked at me and shook his head. After that, there wasn't much more to say. As we parted on the street corner outside the restaurant, however, he shook my hand and held on to it for a moment. "Sometimes I hear of things," he said. "If I do, I'll let you know and I mean that. Don't just drop out of sight again— keep in touch. If you do get located someplace, give me the number."

The first two weeks of December slid by and the streets were saturated with the jouncing rhythm of "Jingle Bells."

What sort of Christmas present do you buy with, say, two dollars for a boy who has been told he will not get his long-promised boat? What do you give a wife who may soon have to hock the little bit of jewelry she does have? A gold-handled nail brush, perhaps, a "delightful whimsey" at forty dollars. Or, for the kids, twenty-five dollars worth of remote-control robot equipped with a voice and a dozen fascinating instruments of destruction?

What had I been given for Christmas in the thin years? It was difficult to remember: a few small toys, a succession of socks and sweaters, an occasional, uncle-bestowed five-dollar bill which was promptly taken away from me to put in the bank, an occasional quarter which was much more exciting because it was mine to spend.

Jing, jing, jing; jing, jing, jing; jingle all the way.

The glittering symbols of prosperity were strewn carelessly across the shop counters, a snowfall of fur and fabric, crystal and silver, gold and plastic and polished wood. I pushed my way from one crowded store to another, peering hopefully into the showcases and wondering how much I should spend.

How much was a dollar worth? To one person it might mean a lot, to the next, very little, but most shoppers knew what value to

put on it. I couldn't know. My margin was shrinking and every bill
I handed across the counter chipped away a day or so. One more
week might find me employed; six more months might not. It was
childhood Christmas again and the quarter I could spend was bigger than the five-dollar bill I could not.

I picked through the jumbled junk on the bargain counters and
learned again that it costs money to be poor. I had seen items
which were good buys at fifty dollars, but most of this muck was
overpriced at one dollar and ninety-eight cents. I would be throwing
my money away if I bought it. There must be some small present
for Janet which was a good value for a couple of dollars; there
must be, and yet there wasn't. As for Cliff, the stores sold nothing,
at any price, which would fill the gap left by the loss of the boat. A
part of his life was gone, and it could not be bought back in any
toy department.

Jingle bells, Jingle bells, deck the halls with unpaid bills. The
scratchy music mocked me as I trudged through the slush from the
stores to the employment agencies, from the employment agencies
to brief, unfruitful interviews. My sadness became misery and my
misery slid into a maudlin self-pity. I saw a split-level Cratchit
family, huddled around the fireplace on Christmas Day, feeding
the flames with fragments of Danish modern furniture. I was
in this mood when Les, making his own regular rounds, stum-
bled into me in the waiting room of an employment agency and
coaxed me out to lunch at the Automat with two other "members
of the club."

One was introduced to me as Ed, a chunky man with crewcut
gray hair, the erstwhile editor of a newspaper which had gone out
of business; the other was Murray, black-haired, neatly dressed
even to a vest with a picket fence of fountain pens ranged across
one of its pockets. A year before he had been an oil company
executive.

"Oil?" I said. "I thought the oil business was booming." All
three men laughed.

"That's our favorite game," Les explained. "It's called 'Find
The Boom.' *Somebody's* making it, that's for sure. Look at the
crowds in the stores; look at the rents in these new apartment
houses. But who are they?"

"Martians?" suggested Murray.

|67|

Les turned to me. "If any business was booming, I would have said it was the ad business. Look at the money it throws around; what about that?"

"The ad business depends on ad budgets," I explained. "And ad budgets come from—well, oil companies and appliance firms, among other people. No budgets, no boom."

Once again we matched experiences. The newspaper editor, fifteen years with one firm and thirteen months out of work, had learned he was unemployed when a competing newspaper phoned to check rumors of the shutdown. His own management announced it three hours later. The oil man, eleven months unemployed, had had a division shot from under him. "Three hundred people at one bang," he added. "It's my own fault, in a way; I did have another job offered me immediately and I turned it down. Didn't see how I could get by on the salary."

"I turned down a couple for the same reason," I said. "It seems funny now."

"But, are you sorry?" asked Les.

"Hell, yes," I answered, and then, "No. I'm not sure. I need the money . . ."

"I'm not," announced Murray. "I need the money, too—boy how I need it—but I don't think I'm sorry. What's the point of working my way up again and then finding myself out in the street, even ten years older? I'd rather take my beating now." He slid one of the pens from his vest pocket, almost unconsciously it seemed, and tapped on the table with it to emphasize his point.

"But that could happen to you in any job," I objected.

"That isn't what he meant," Ed explained, and Murray nodded. The ex-editor ran his hand over his close-cropped gray hair and then continued. "I think what Murray meant is something like this: You can't relive your life and it's a mistake to go looking for the job you lost, or an imitation of it. The trick is not to sell what you have, but to have what will sell. You take me, for example. I'm not sure I'd go back to the newspaper business if I could. *My* newspaper business is dying and I belong to its past. In some other line, who knows? I could be the man of the future. I might make a good copywriter for an ad agency. I spent most of my life writing short, punchy heads, you know. Maybe I could bring some new ideas to the ad business."

|68|

"No reflection on you," I said, "but it would be the height of irony if you landed a good agency spot with no experience at all. I can't, with all my years in the business."

Les laughed. "You're catching on," he said. "That's the way it often happens. I wouldn't go back either, because I think my ex-employers are ossifying. They're reaching the point where they can't adapt to change and that can be fatal. I'm being forced to adapt and it may be the luckiest thing which ever happened to me. There's a lot of new, small firms springing up; they've got ideas and imagination and they're flexible; what they need is people with experience that they can afford to hire. I've got a hunch I'm going to be one of those people."

The lunch broke up on this optimistic note. Ed announced that he had a dentist appointment, Les left to do some telephoning, and Murray mentioned Christmas shopping. "Good luck," I said bitterly. "I've combed every store in New York and I haven't bought a thing."

Murray glanced at me. "Every store in New York?" he repeated. "You mean in your New York—midtown New York."

"Well, I . . ."

"You know," he said, waving his hand in the general direction of the crowded street, "a lot of people haven't been invited to this great big party. Ever wonder where they do their Christmas shopping? If you want to come along, I'll show you."

We dived into the subway and came up in a section of town I had never seen before. The streets were narrower and the small shops were packed together in block-long rows—toys, clothes, hardware, food, liquor, radios. The crowds swirled in little eddies along the streets, flowing out of one store and into the next, and small knots of people gathered around the sidewalk pitchmen. We stopped for a moment to watch one. "I'd just like a word with the ladies in the crowd," he was saying. "Do you have a whole kitchen drawer full of knives? Well, ladies, you know that one good man is worth a dozen bums and I'm telling you one good knife is worth that drawerful. Yes, sir! You may never find the all-purpose man but you've found the all-purpose knife, ladies, right here on this street corner. Now, if you want to prepare attractive meals . . ." He sliced the top from a tomato and, with a few deft cuts, shaped it into a rosette. "Now, then, ladies, my hand isn't quicker than your

|69|

eye; you just watch closely and I'll show you how it's done . . ."

We moved on. "I know a man who gets twenty thousand a year for doing the same thing," said Murray. "It all depends on where you set up your stand. Let's try this store."

Shelves and bins; rough wood counters, heaped-up merchandise and good-humored faces, white, black, brown and yellow.

"Hold on," said Murray. "Here's something for my little girl." He picked a small, gaily painted wooden box from the counter and lifted the lid, triggering a tinkly little tune. "She loves these things," he explained. "She can sit and listen to them by the hour. I paid fifteen bucks for one last year, but it isn't the box which counts, it's the music." I glanced at the card on the counter. The box cost one dollar.

We explored the shelves. "You have to have a sharp eye," Murray explained, poking among some gaudy glassware. "Some very nice stuff gets buried under all this—ah ha!" He pulled out a square white box plastered with lurid red and gold decorations, and turned it over to examine the sticker on the bottom. "Two-fifty," he said. "Now, if your wife has a dressing table . . ."

My face must have reflected my feelings because he laughed and held the box closer. "Paper," he explained, running his fingernail under the edge of the decorations. "Soak it off and that's Italian alabaster underneath. I don't know why they do things like that; too plain for some people without it, I guess." I bought the box.

We pushed our way from store to store, rooting through the bins of junk and picking out the occasional gem. I was fascinated to see year-old fads set out for sale. "This is where they end up," said Murray, pointing to an "executive" ashtray priced at ninety-five cents. The last time I had seen it, uptown, the tag had read five dollars. With Skip in mind, I examined a large box labeled "Visits to Foreign Lands." It was selling for a dollar and contained a phonograph record of children's songs from other countries, and a set of color slides. I hesitated over it. We had a record player but no slide projector. "Buy it," Murray advised. "There's a place down the street where you can get a good plastic viewer for sixty cents."

By five o'clock I had spent twelve dollars, an appalling amount, but I had an armload of packages. "It takes a lot of time to do it this way," Murray shouted over the roar of the subway as we rode toward Grand Central. "But that's the whole idea; you spend time to save cash. Most of us have more time than money anyway."

One problem remained unsolved—a present for Cliff. I paid two more visits to Murray's marketplace and debated a dozen possibilities, but nothing seemed sufficient. In the end, I marched grimly into a midtown department store and bought a miniature road-racing set, trying not to think of all the things the cost represented. It came to more than I had spent on presents for both Janet and Skip.

We rolled out of bed Christmas morning determined to have a happy day. The pile of presents looked woefully small, but Janet set to work energetically to fill the gap with activity. "This is something I used to do in Illinois," she declared, displaying a needle and a long length of thread. She strung some popcorn and then handed it over to Skip so he could paint the kernels with his water colors. I set up the road-race after Cliff had opened it and he ran the cars around the track a few times. I suggested some races, but he said "Later, maybe" and wandered out of the house, presumably to visit his friends. It was a good Christmas and we had a good time, and I got through the entire day—almost—without wishing that it hadn't come up at this particular time.

It was the season of suburban parties and we ducked most of them so we wouldn't have to issue invitations in return. On New Year's Eve, however, we left the kids with Margie and Mel and went to Max Weltchek's get-together. He had filled his house with a large and oddly assorted crowd: a few mutual friends, who drank martinis; some colleagues from the hardware trade who preferred bourbon; and a group of hard-handed fishermen who downed red wine. For some reason I settled on bourbon. It was a good party; in fact, it was one of the best New Year's Eve parties I had been to in a long time, and when midnight came I clicked my glass against Janet's and I said, "It's been a lousy year—good riddance to it."

"Here's to next year," she answered. "Here's to a good one."

"Here's to a good one," I echoed. "Wherever it ends."

Four Men
at a Table

"Why?" said the ex-office manager. "Why us, why me?"

"Any ketchup over on your side?" asked the ex-oil man.

"Why?" repeated the ex-editor. "Why not? A flower pot falls off a window sill. There are fifty people walking along the sidewalk underneath and it kills one of them. Why him?"

"Salt, too, if you don't mind," said the ex-oil man.

"That's no answer," I objected. "The four of us represent about eighty years' accumulated experience. All the guys like us; they represent thousands of years and the community is throwing it all away. Why?"

"Don't want it," said the ex-oil man, between bites of his sandwich. "Liability. Everyone has a cost problem. Take your eye off costs for a minute and they run away with you. So, let's suppose you hear some guy is going to retire or shift to another job. You go hot-footing around to make a bid for the opening and . . ."

"There isn't any opening," the ex-office manager finished.

"You know it. Maybe they move an assistant up to replace this guy and then someone else up to replace the assistant and then someone else up to replace him and the vacancy gets pushed down the line until it disappears in the mailroom someplace. All the chairs are filled and nobody notices there's one less man. Or maybe they just eliminate the job and scatter the work around the shop. The product is one per cent lousier and the cost is one per cent higher but who notices? The consumer is getting prosperity as a premium with every package. So who needs experience?"

"They're scared of costs," said the ex-editor. "I go along with you there—but I think that's only part of it. They're scared, period."

"Of what?"

"Everything, anything, they don't even know. They're scared of costs and scared of competition. They're scared of depression and scared of inflation and scared of Russia and most of all, I think, they're scared of America. They're afraid of the energetic new companies, fighting their way up. They're afraid of their customers and their own employees and some guy talking raw truth on a street corner. They're afraid of their leaders and appalled at the idea of doing any leading themselves. They build their private little worlds to shut out their own country and its frightening energy and its idealism. And then we blow in and bring that world with us. So—they're afraid of us."

"Not me," said the ex-office manager. "All I want to do is go home. I'm on their side."

"Oh, no you're not," said the ex-editor, taking off his glasses and pointing with them across the table. "Not any more. You've been shopping around and seeing a bit of the world. You've been picking up bits and pieces—words, expressions, gestures. *You* may not realize it, but you're alien to them now, you're *different*. Haven't you gone in for an interview with your old buddies and found you just couldn't seem to get through to them . . .?"

"Well, I'm damned," I said.

"I see *you* have. The 'why' is simple enough. You can't belong to the club any more because you've all been outside. You've peeked behind the scenery. They just don't want people around who've learned there's a hole in the bottom of the affluent society."

"This is all too complicated for me," said the ex-office manager, "but I don't think you have to be a psychologist to figure out what scares them. They look at us and they know what happened to us could happen to them. Tomorrow, maybe."

"There's three theories," said the ex-editor, and they all looked at me.

|74|

"I'm not sure I've got any," I said. "Not yet, anyway. I can't help feeling that in some way a lot of it's my own fault. We're all being hurt by these attitudes you've talked about, but then we all helped to create them. That word 'executive'; it was sort of a . . . a badge I pinned on. I think more than anything else it was something to hang on to at all costs. It occurs to me now that maybe it carried a price tag. I can think of things—ideas and policies and things like that—which I wished I'd fought for and some things I should have fought against. If I'd won, we all might be better off. If I'd lost, the worst that could have happened is that I'd be . . ."

"Where you are anyway," said the ex-editor.

"I guess that's what I mean. The funny thing is that I wasn't always that way. There was a time once . . . . No, I guess that's something else again." For a moment it had become mixed up with the war and the tanks, with the roar of engines and the smell of hot oil and the gritty feel of desert sand. My neck could never be that far out again; not in any office, not for any reason.

JANUARY
"It's the Next Thing to Charity"

January is the job hunter's enemy, the street-dweller's foe. January is a wet, gray creature which crawls out of the gutter to paw your polished shoes and splash you with dirty spray from the wheels of contemptuous taxis. January is the harsh wind which sweeps the people from the streets into their nests, robbing the nestless even of that thin illusion of belonging. January is the time-stealer which turns "last month" into "last year." When did you leave your last employment? Recently? A few weeks ago? A couple of months ago? Last year, last year, last year.

"Could you do anything with the electric iron?" I asked Janet. It was the third day after the New Year and I had come home with the cuffs of my newly pressed trousers soggy and shapeless.

"Not really. They wouldn't look right and besides, I'd just be ironing the dirt into them. I could fix them up for ordinary purposes, maybe—you could get by. But for interviews and stuff . . ."

"Okay," I said wearily. "Shove them into the cleaners."

"Well, then, since I'm going anyway, that overcoat . . ."

"No. Just forget about the overcoat." A few more weeks and I could get by without it; meanwhile, I could always slip out of it in the reception room and carry it over my arm. It cost money to clean an overcoat.

That's the way we saved and a stupid, pointless, futile way it was, too. I cut down on cigarettes; Janet trudged dutifully upstairs to turn off the light in the bathroom. It was the thriftiness of Victorian legend, the hoarded candlestubs which became the foundation of a fortune. It saved, possibly, enough money to pay for the postage stamps when I mailed out checks for taxes, mortgage installments and insurance premiums. Hew the logs I might, and raise the roof with my bare hands, but this wouldn't knock one nickel off the property taxes once the cabin was completed. We were squeezed in that twentieth-century thumbscrew, the irreducible cost, and the answer was not to save pennies, but to earn dollars.

The worry of big debts was a dull ache, the meanness of small economies a vicious sting. Skip came home with a mimeographed sheet about the school pageant, in which he would play a Continental soldier. Costumes could be purchased locally, but details were obligingly supplied "for the benefit of those parents who cared to make them at home."

"Well," said Janet, "I could do it easily enough, but . . ."

"I thought we were through spending money to put up a front."

"It's Skip's front as well as ours. You know what children are like. Besides, it's an investment like . . . like picking up checks in the bar car."

"All right," I said, "but what a *hell* of a way to look at it."

How did we ever get boxed in like this, I wondered, sorting through the bills. Ten dollars here, fifty dollars there, one hundred and sixty-eight dollars and seventeen cents and all spent purely to maintain our momentum, all shoveled out in big chunks before we had put one piece of bread on the plate to feed ourselves. Food, clothes, heat, shelter—these are the first concerns of the besieged family and they came last on our budget list, bought with whatever pennies could be shaken out by our silly little economies. Even the uniform for Skip's pageant had significance far beyond a child's pleasure.

"It stinks," I said.

"What stinks?" asked Janet.

"The whole damn business stinks. I was a Pilgrim, in the school Thanksgiving pageant. We made our own costume; almost everyone did. A few people bought them and we felt sorry for them because it was a thing for the *kids*. It was for the *kids*. It was part of the fun, making them."

"If it worries you that much . . ."

"Let it go," I said. "It doesn't." It did though; it was a cheap game played by childish people who could find no deeper concerns in a wounded world. This is how Max sees us, I thought; this is why he always says only half of what he thinks. We look down our sophisticated noses at him and he looks at a bunch of spoiled brats pushing each other in the playground, and dealing out mean little hurts. This is how Phil sees us and that battered briefcase is his own private little joke on all of us. And yet they both love us and how they do it, God only knows, except that there must be some dimension to that word "bigness" which never was mentioned in the corporate pamphlets.

We sold the big car. "Let's do it now, while we've still got some cash left," Janet suggested. "They can always tell when you're desperate and they can beat you down." They beat us down anyway at three different used car lots. "You want my advice," said the third dealer. "You put an ad in the paper and unload it on some private buyer. You get a bit more that way, maybe; I can't go no higher." We juggled this suggestion for a couple of days and then took it, hoping that none of our neighbors would show up in search of a second car. The ad drew two dealers, a station wagon full of teen-agers who made contemptuous remarks and then roared away, an indecisive schoolteacher and finally a huge, over-alled factory foreman who examined the car minutely and then said, "Okay." We watched it roll out of the driveway with a stranger at the wheel.

"Well," said Janet. "That's one less set of repair bills."

"It's a good thing we sold it while it was still running." I was thinking of all the other things we owned which hummed and buzzed and clicked and, on occasion, broke down. We couldn't afford to repair or replace any of them. One by one they would stop working and we would live in a dying house. In the end, perhaps, we would be cooking our food in the fireplace and washing our clothes in the bath tub, surrounded by the gleaming metal and plastic hulks of our useless machines.

Money made things move. It meant so little when you had it

and when you didn't have it, the gap had to be filled with time and plodding effort and embarrassed evasions. Just a few coins, handed to a taxi driver, would double the number of calls I could make in a day. Just a few bits of green paper would start the dead machinery whirring again. Money had ceased to have any importance as a badge of rank; now it was a working tool. It was no longer the stuff which bought carriage lamps and drinks at the country club; it was a propellant; it was the fuel which gave you the opportunity to be effective. A few thousand of those bits of paper—two or three more little numbers in the bankbook—and there could be a new advertising agency on Madison Avenue; a tough little agency which would bear down on the big boys like a pirate brig cutting across the bows of a fat merchantman. I had the ideas now and—I knew where I could get the men.

In spite of this philosophy, or possibly because of it, the urge to extravagance remained. More than that, it became a psychological itch. I found myself staring in shop windows and even prowling through the aisles of department stores, fighting the impulse to buy some useless piece of junk. I wanted to spend money; I wanted to show everyone—myself and the bored, anonymous girl behind the counter that I still *could* spend money. I wanted to take home something which wasn't a necessity, something which was magnificently useless. Give up spending? It would be easier to give up smoking.

In mid-January, Janet found a job.

"Max's place!" I said. "When you said a job I thought you meant a *job*. Somebody we didn't know. This is . . . God dammit, this is the next thing to charity!"

"But . . ."

"No. Absolutely not!"

"If you'd just . . ."

"I'd rather just walk up to Max and tell him honestly that we're broke and ask for a loan. It would be a hell of a lot less embarrassing. I said no and I mean it and that's that."

And that remained that for two hours. Then Max dropped in and dismantled my objections, quietly and candidly, with the air of a man taking apart an engine. "Certainly I'm doing you a favor," he said. "I've got some business and I'm tossing it your way because I know you could use it. It won't be the first time I've done it. It won't be the last, either."

"It's the Next Thing
to Charity"

"Now, look, Max," I began. "I do appreciate it, but . . ."

"Oh, hell, why don't you save everyone's time and agree now instead of two days from now? I need part-time help and it isn't easy to find in this town. Girls want full-time jobs and, if they are any good, they head for the city anyway. I need somebody like Janet and it might as well *be* Janet."

"Well, I . . ."

"Couple of other points," Max continued, relentlessly. "The work is a lot more interesting than spending time in some real estate office would be. From my viewpoint, it means having someone on hand I can trust. It works out well all around."

"It works out lousy," I told him. "You know as well as I do that mixing business and personal relationships—neighborhood relationships too—is just asking for trouble. Suppose Janet wants to quit at an awkward time for you? Okay, it happens all the time, but not between people who still meet at the same parties. It's . . . it's always been one of the basic rules—don't do business with your neighbors."

"And a very good one, too," said Max, blandly. "I'm in favor of it. Now you tell *me;* why did you move up here in the first place?"

"Well, the kids . . . we needed the space . . ."

"You can get that in a dozen other suburbs. Why do you people haunt the bar car on the train? Why do your firms push you into neighborhood associations and community projects? It's mainly so all of you can sell things to each other. I don't like it; I never did like it, but that's the way the world spins these days and if I can't cure it, I may as well take advantage of it. Janet could be a good deal of help to us."

"You realize it would be only until . . . only temporary?"

"I realize that. She can quit anytime and nobody will be hurt; it would simply put me back where I am now." Max heaved himself out of the easy chair. "Let's drop the subject; you talk it over and let me know."

I prowled around the living room for several minutes after he left and Janet simply sat and waited.

"Dammit," I said, "I *still* don't think . . ."

I sat down beside her on the sofa. "Now look," I said, "it just seems to me . . ."

But that wasn't what I wanted to say, either.

"All right," I said. "What do *you* think?"

|81|

"I think I should take it. Besides . . ."

"Besides what?"

"I *did* think this over myself, you know. I thought it over pretty thoroughly. Like you say, like Max says, it isn't the best idea in the world. I can see that for myself. It just happens that nothing else is likely to be very satisfactory either and we could do a lot worse. I didn't say anything, but you've been playing the Victorian husband all evening. *My* wife won't do this and I haven't decided whether *my* wife should do that."

"The point is whether it's a good thing to mix business and . . ."

"I know that and that's why I didn't get sore. But I think my opinion counts too—especially since I'm the one who'd actually be taking the job."

I'd been caught off base and I knew it. The whole business still seemed unwise but there was one argument which did make a lot of sense: what else was there? A few stores, perhaps; a handful of local insurance and law offices which would hardly be in the market for part-time temporary help.

"Okay," I said. "There was an objection which ought to be raised and I've raised it. If it doesn't worry Max or you, I guess it doesn't worry me."

And so Janet got up in the morning, drove me to the station, returned home for the kids, dropped them off at school and then went to work.

The immediate effect of shedding one car and adding one small income was to check the frightening drain on the bank account. It still dwindled, but it dwindled at a slower pace and I could add up my grim little time chart and postpone doomsday by a few more weeks. A brighter picture on paper, but only on paper.

I had to face the fact that my contacts were fading too; my list of possibilities was becoming dog-eared and outdated. With each week the field narrowed and the round of calls became more routine. Jerry's firm came off the list. "I couldn't let you get your hopes up," Jerry said honestly, "and I wouldn't want you to waste your time. Please drop in whenever you want to, but . . . you understand." I did understand and I was grateful to Jerry, who was taking something of a chance in even hinting that his outfit was tightening up on personnel. Abbott and Costello slipped into the past. They were still polite when I called, but it was obvious that they weren't going to hire me and that my welcome was wearing thin. The major expansions, the new projects, the expected openings continued to remain just around the corner and just out of reach. Each week I phoned for appointments and each week some voice said, "Why—uh—I'm sort of tied up this week. I—uh—that is, there hasn't been any change since the last time you were up here. We'll give you a call if there is; I don't think we need to bother you otherwise. Goodbye." One by one, I crossed them off.

My shoes grew shabby and I replaced them, but the shabbiness seemed to linger over the new pair and over my carefully pressed suits, my clean shirts and my new neckties. Something oozed from my pores like sweat and stained them—that invisible something called "seediness"—and one day, when I looked in the mirror, I saw the face of Les. The tight lines at the corner of the mouth were there and the eyes which stayed grim even when the lips smiled. It was a face seen behind the cut-rate counter or bending over an untidy sample case filled with cheap notions; the face of a man who works without purpose and lives without hope, a man who wishes each week done until he has wished his life away.

There were days—a good many of them now—which could have been spent at home. I dialed my way through what was left of the list. Nothing. I phoned some friends, merely to suggest a social lunch. Tied up, out of town, can't make it, nothing. And still I hung around, nursing one beer at the bar at Philippe's at lunch time, riding the commuter special home, hoping for that chance encounter which might open a door. From my childhood days there had never been enough time; now time was a burden. Three P.M. My ankles ached and there was no place to sit down; not in hurrying New York. The wind was whipping sleet through the streets and it was no day for strolling. I could have visited the coffee shop, but that meant ordering something. I could have gone to the newsreel theater, but that meant paying admission. I could have taken the early train home, but that meant I had given up for the day. I wandered through the station, looking at the window displays I already knew by heart. There was an advertising film running in one shop and I watched it all the way through. Fun in beautiful Florida; water-skiing, boating, skin-diving, swimming, dancing in the evening on the cocktail terrace. Where today's smart young executive goes to relax from his burden of responsibility. I trudged up the stairs to the drug store for some browsing among the paperback books. There were no new ones; the display hadn't been changed for a couple of weeks now and I'd read all of them, a couple of pages at a time, right there at the book rack. There were still a couple of men I hadn't been able to reach that afternoon and there were phone booths in the drug store. How long since I had tried Mr. X? Half an hour; almost thirty-five minutes, actually. I tried him again, but he was still in the meeting and perhaps if you could tell me what you're calling him about . . . I hung up and thought about Mr. Y. I tried him just a few minutes before, at 3 P.M., but you never know. I dialed the number, but he was still tied up on the other line. What the hell did he have to spend an hour on the phone for, or however long it had been? How long *had* it been? I hiked down the stairs again and out into the waiting room where I could see the big clock. Three-fifteen. I started prowling again. There must be somebody I hadn't tried; somebody, someplace, who still didn't know I was available.

And so the list shrank through the last days of January—all the old contacts, all the old acquaintances, all the people I had once dealt with briefly or met casually, every name in my memory and every name in my files. I had dredged the advertising business to its bottom, right down to the one-client, two-men-and-a-girl agencies. I had bounced off the advertising department of every firm where I had friends or friends of friends or an entree of any sort. Everyone knew I was available and no matter how often I called them, they weren't calling me.

The last week in January the list ran out. I made two calls on Monday, had lunch with Phil on Tuesday and lined up an appointment for Wednesday morning. There was nothing exciting about the appointment; it was a small company which seemed to need an assistant advertising director. I couldn't find out whether a vacancy actually existed and the voice on the other end of the line said dubiously, "The salary we're offering . . . a man of your experience, I mean." Well, I answered cheerfully, it wouldn't do any harm to talk it over and the voice agreed that no, it certainly wouldn't do any harm. Wednesday morning we did talk it over. The salary was about right for a twenty-five-year-old kid and I was ready to take it; it was just that much more than nothing at all. I tried to finesse the obvious question—why was I willing to work so cheap—and I did it very badly and on that note the interview ended.

That was the last lead and when I walked out into the street there was nothing left, nothing at all. There was no place to go and no one to call; there was nothing to set up for Thursday or Friday or next week or next month. The weather was cold and clear. I walked over to the park and sat down on a bench in the sunlight which was so bright and had so little warmth.

There had to be a reason. Men failed because they drank or they made mistakes or they lacked the brains or the energy or the ambition to get ahead. They failed, as we used that word in the suburbs, and yet many of them worked someplace and took home a pay check, however small, at the end of a week. Poor old Jake, we used to say; still knocking together routine copy for minor accounts after all these years. And yet even poor old Jake could point to something; he was in the business, he drew down a salary, he was consulted on rare occasions and when people spoke of him personally he was good old Jake because he was popular. Poor, good old Jake was what I had never intended to be, and yet, a man could do a lot worse in this life than to have a job and an income and work which he liked and people who liked him. He was still an advertising man and I wasn't.

Every morning I was surrounded by thousands of people streaming through the streets to work. Bankers and bartenders, welders and waitresses, models and messengers, platoons of young men off the Ivy League racks and now, my own wife. They all *belonged* some place. The fumbling young man who sold me a necktie and didn't know his own stock, the waitress who slung my lunch on the table so hard that the plate nearly broke, the taxidriver who made me late for an appointment because he couldn't find the address—had I less to offer than *any* of them?

Was I unemployable?

I sat in the park until train time and then I went home with the big question still unanswered—what now? Should I go into the city on Thursday and Friday and what would I accomplish if I did? I went, and with a brassiness born of desperation I phoned four or five of the people who had made it clear they didn't want to hear from me again. Two of them—to their eternal credit—were polite.

|85|

I also phoned Phil on the off-chance he might be free for lunch, but he was out of town. A hot dog in the station or a sandwich at the Automat? A vision of sandwich *and* soup—a lunch which could be dragged out—drifted through my mind and I trudged over to the Automat. Les and the ex-oilman were sitting at the table by the window.

"The round table is shrinking," said the ex-oilman as I sat down. "Our journalistic friend has crossed the tracks. He found a job."

"That's swell! Where?"

"You might as well treat this as funny; you'll feel better. His hunch was right. He landed a spot with an ad agency, in their public relations department."

"It's funny," I said.

"How's it going with you?"

"Oh, all right, I guess." I should have stopped there, perhaps, but I didn't and the whole story came out, down through the dying list and ending at the park bench. "I'm sorry," I said. "You've both got your own troubles. There's no point in unloading mine on you."

"Maybe not," said the ex-oilman. "On the other hand, maybe there is."

"It's just that . . . well, I'm feeling pretty close to panic, I guess. What do I do now?"

"What do you do?" repeated Les. He leaned back in his chair and smiled. "Why, you start job-hunting, of course."

"You Wouldn't Like to Go to Chicago, Would You?"

This is where the pavement really begins to hurt under your feet, where you run down all the leads, where you write to blind box numbers and get no reply, where you tramp around to employment agencies and sit with teen-aged stenos and would-be "Gal Fridays" waiting to be processed, where you ride sooty little trains through the industrial suburbs to factories beside smoking slag heaps. This is where you rise each morning and shave and stuff your briefcase full of résumés and take the train to nowhere.

This is "job-hunting" as Les used the phrase; this is what the ex-editor meant when he said, "You don't sell what you have; you have what will sell." You spread out the "Help Wanted" pages and work your way down the columns of fine print, one tiny item after another: accountant, bookkeeper, credit investigator, construction worker, janitor, loom operator, messenger, office manager—that's you—printer, repairman, rigger, salesman—that's you, too—tabulator, welder, wrapper, writer . . . writer? Well, what can you lose by trying? "Promotion specialist, extensive consumer product experience, fluent Spanish . . ." Check it out, there's always the chance you can talk your way around that language requirement. This was getting down to bedrock with a vengeance and, as the ex-oil man put it, "Hell, I'd answer an ad for a violinist. Maybe they'd have some other job going and if they didn't, I'd pick up a fiddle and have a try."

It was a strange, tough business; it was job-hunting with only one goal—to get in off the street, to find a toe-hold someplace in the working community. Les launched me that day in the Automat; when he and the ex-oil man unfolded a newspaper and began dredging its pages.

"There's nothing there," I told them. "I looked."

"Did you, now?" said Les. "Let's see. Ummm . . . 'Production coordinator.' How's that?"

"I don't even know what it is."

The ex-oil man shrugged. "A man who coordinates production, obviously. You've coordinated things, haven't you?"

"Well . . . yes, in a way. But . . ."

"All coordination is alike," said the ex-oil man, searching in his vest pocket and selecting a pen with red ink. "The experts do the work and you keep them from beating each others' brain out. Otherwise, you sit around drawing up schedules and then revising them if things don't work out that way."

"I still don't. . . ."

"Look," said Les, "if you're ever offered a good job; grab it. By the time they find out you don't know anything about it, you will."

"Remember whatzisname?" added the ex-oil man. "The thin guy with glasses who used to be in the cosmetic business? He spotted an ad for a sales analyst one morning and he didn't have anything else lined up for the day so he figured what the hell and took a crack at it and they hired him. He worked there for a month and then he landed something which was a bit more in his line, so he moved on."

"What did it involve?" I asked. "Actually working as a sales analyst, I mean?"

"He never did find out," said the ex-oilman. "He spent that month filling out forms and passing around memos. That reminds me, incidentally; you always want to remember that companies frequently hire guys for certain skills and then never use them. That's why I say I'd take a job as a violinist. The chances are they'd say something like, 'We're anxious to hear you play, of course, but just put the violin in the corner for a moment and help us straighten out these box office receipts.' The next thing you know I'd be doing it full time. If I really *were* a violinist, you see, it would be rough. The point is that the same thing works in reverse. If I took a job I know something about, in the oil business . . ."

"They might hand you a violin," I said.

"It could happen," said the ex-oil man gloomily.

"Here's one," Les interrupted, taking the oil man's pen and circling an ad. "Sales promotion. Assistant director. Um . . let's see now . . . 'energetic, ambitious, self-starter' . . . so on and so forth. That means they don't intend to pay very much; if they were offering a good salary they'd take all that for granted . . . . emphasis on dealer relations; you should be good at that angle. No other information. That probably means they want a kid, or they'd specify experience. Why don't you have a crack at it anyway, just to pick up some seasoning? Sort of a dry run."

We plowed our way through the entire page, my two companions offering a running commentary as we moved from ad to ad: "Nope . . . nope . . . nope . . . industrial salesman; nope . . . nope . . . nope . . . this outfit's been running the same ad for months now; don't know why. Steer clear of them, there's something wrong there. . . ."

"Why would they do that?" I asked.

"Who knows? Can't find the perfect man, maybe. More likely they're rounding up commission salesmen and have worded their ad to make it look like a staff opening so they'll get more experienced applicants. Where were we, now? . . . nope . . . nope . . . oh, here's a possibility, but don't follow it up unless you're really desperate." That firm, I learned, had a reputation for picking up good men who had to get in off the street quickly and driving them brutally for miserable wages. "They're smart bastards," said Les. "You have to hand them that. They know there's a gold-mine of talent pounding the pavements. They scoop 'em in and get $20,000 worth of work and ideas for peanuts." In the end, we dredged out four ads and I went to work on them.

"Sales promotion. Assistant director." The ad led me to an employment agency in a midtown side street; one of those oddly neglected side streets which seems to exist on borrowed time among the excavations and the towering new glass-walled skyscrapers. I found the address with some difficulty—it was a narrow door pinched between two cut-rate shops—and I stood on the sidewalk for a moment, undecided. From the second floor up, the building was solidly Victorian, a quietly crumbling mass of grimy gray stone with decorative lintels over the tall, unwashed windows. The ground floor had been "modernized" with corrugated aluminum facing, a pathetic gesture which destroyed whatever weary dignity the building might have possessed. Like the tired, gray men who passed through its sagging door, the building tried to draw the eye away from its seamed face by donning a gaudy necktie. Like those men, it had failed, for it could not be young and it would not be mature.

Well, hell; I had to start some place.

There was no lobby, merely a narrow corridor painted institutional green, with a small directory and a massive, aluminum-painted radiator which hissed maliciously as I squeezed past it. The automatic elevator, obviously another consequence of the "modernizing" process, was about the size of a small closet and the floor gave alarmingly as I stepped into it. I tapped the button and nothing happened. I ground my thumb into it vigorously; the door closed in a series of jerks and the elevator bounded upward with a sudden resiliency, like a ball on the end of a rubber cord. It stopped abruptly and the door slid back about eight inches. I pushed it open the rest of the way, stepped out into another green-painted corridor and found myself facing a frosted glass door with the employment agency's name lettered on it in black-edged gilt.

The waiting room was long, narrow, windowless and painted the same shade of green as the corridors. Two wooden benches, placed end to end, filled one wall and a heavy table with four or five straight chairs had been placed along the other. At the near end of the room, next to the entrance, an insecure floor lamp-table leaned against the wall, at the far end a battered desk, manned by a middle-aged woman, barred the path to a glass door beyond. I refolded my copy of the newspaper to bring their ad on the outside and cleared my throat.

Her practised eye gave me a quick up-and-down survey from hair to tie to jacket to attaché case and newspaper to shoes. She had seen my type before, that was obvious. Surplus executive, big ideas, small placement potential. Couldn't make it with his own connections; wants us to do it for him. Six of him don't add up to one good shorthand typist.

"Ya filled outa card?"

"Well, I thought possibly that . . ."

"Fill outa card."

"But I'm not sure this opening . . ."

"Card."

There was a box of them at the table. I sat down, picked one out and filled it in—name, address, phone number, position required, previous positions held. There was, at the bottom, the usual printed reminder that New York state law banned discrimination because of age. I handed the card to the guardian of the gates and sat down on one of the benches to wait my turn.

There were four other people ahead of me and I drifted into the old subway rider's game, studying each one and trying to guess who they were and what had brought them to this dreary room. The two buxom, black-haired girls, a-wriggle with their whispered conversation, they would be typists. This was a mere errand for them. They had left one office because the work was too dull or the supply of unmarried men too limited; they were merely stopping off on their way to another where the work would be much the same but the hunting might be better. Neither curiosity about the job nor doubt about the interview troubled them; if they could type they'd be hired. Pain and discouragement, fear and bitterness; these still lay too far in their future to be glimpsed from a bench in the employment office.

The well-dressed Negro sitting next to them, a briefcase resting on his knees, probably was in his early thirties. What was in the briefcase? A college degree, perhaps; an honorable discharge from the Army, possibly even an officer's commission. Records, clippings, ideas, plans and a prayer: Look at what I can do, look at what I have done. They called him "Mister" in New York; they shook his hand and listened to his story and accepted his application and invited him to lunch in their executive dining room but they did not hire him. There was nothing he could fight because there was no one who hated him and no one who opposed him; there was just the caution of men who didn't want to be the first.

Next to the young Negro, a girl or a woman, it was hard to say; she could be anywhere between twenty-seven and thirty-two. Light

|91|

gray tailored suit; inconspicuous hat; plain, black, high-heeled shoes; small, neat attaché case. Our Miss Somebody, happily wedded to her career until now. What incompatibility had broken up that match? It had been a small firm, perhaps, a tight little family which had been scattered by failure or a merger. Or, possibly, she had delivered the sort of ultimatum which might work with a husband, but didn't work with a corporation. Like me, she was on unfamiliar territory and she was nervous. Her gaze wandered around the room, from the desk at the end to the table to the discouraged floor lamp to the other occupants of the room. She caught my eye, smiled tentatively, then flushed and glanced away.

Through the next half an hour or so, I hitched my way slowly down the bench toward the sanctum behind the glass doors. The two stenos went in and came out five minutes later, trotting purposefully through the room, still chattering. The young Negro went in and emerged after ten minutes, his face an unreadable blank. Our Miss Somebody got ten minutes and came out biting her lip. She stood in the middle of the room for a few seconds, looking at the woman behind the desk and then at me. Then she dropped a wadded-up copy of the want-ad section on the table and bolted through the door.

It was my turn.

The glass door led to a tiny ante-room and I hesitated for a moment; there were two small offices opening off it, both with their doors partly closed.

"In here," said a sharp voice and I pushed open the right-hand door. The office was lined with dark green file cabinets and furnished with a desk and two straight chairs. A single window bearing the word YCNEGA overlooked the street; presumably the first half of the name was lettered on the window of the other office.

"Good morning," I said. "I came about your ad in the paper, the sales promotion job. I think perhaps . . ."

"Card," said the man behind the desk. I handed it to him with a copy of my résumé and he studied both, tapping on the blotter with his fingers. I waited a few seconds and then sat down in one of the straight chairs without an invitation.

"Advertising," he said, finally. "No sales promotion here."

"I know, but I thought . . ."

"Opening's for a sales promotion man. Experienced. Their product line."

"Well, what *is* their product line? I've handled several, you know; it could be something I've got a pretty good background in."

"You're not qualified. Get any advertising jobs, we'll let you know."

"Shouldn't they be the ones to decide that?" I asked. "What makes you so sure they wouldn't be interested? Maybe they would. And if they aren't, all they have to do is say no."

"Can't send them unqualified men."

I digested this for a moment.

"Who pays your fee?" I asked. "Me or the employer?"

"You do. It's on the card. Unless it's some outfit which refunds fees. This isn't."

"Then I don't understand what you mean by 'sending them' applicants. If I pay the fee aren't you my agent? Aren't you acting for *me?*"

"Get any openings for someone with your background, we'll let you know," he said doggedly. There was a long silence and the interview was obviously at an end.

"Okay," I said, standing up. "Thanks."

The waiting room had filled up again; there were six people sitting on the benches as I walked through. In the corridor, I tapped the elevator button; then remembered and ground my thumb into it like a man squashing a beetle. It was early noon and the other guys might be having lunch at the Automat. I needed desperately to hear a friendly human voice.

There were exact duplicates of that building and that waiting room all over New York and through the next few weeks I sat on many benches, filled out many cards, walked away from many interviews with that feeling of sick desperation. A couple of months before I had picked my agencies; now I was pulled into all of them, from the best to the worst. "You don't have to tell me," said the ex-oilman. "I ought to be used to it, but I'm not. Every time I leave some of those places I feel like heading straight for the river and jumping in. You go in and put what you have on their desk, whatever it is, and they tell you it isn't worth a damn. Or maybe it's just this feeling I always get that they don't think there's a hope in hell of placing me and they don't intend to waste their time trying. I wouldn't go near that type if I didn't have to because of the ads."

That was the catch, those "Help Wanted" ads. They said "salesman" or "marketing specialist" or even "assistant advertising manager" and they gave the name of the employment agency, not the company. You had to follow them up—you had to follow *any* possibility up—and so there you were again, filling out another card in another drab waiting room, facing another curt, uninterested man who was saying, "They wouldn't want you; opening's for a frozen foods salesman; get anything for a beverage salesman, we'll let you know." Perhaps a week or so later you saw an ad for "salesman, beverage" placed by this same agency and you wondered why they hadn't called you. Perhaps you phoned them to find out and they said "job's filled" and hung up. They glanced at the cards and skimmed through the résumés and made some comment and whatever they actually said, your ultra-sensitive ear picked up a contemptuous overtone: why are you wasting our time, why don't you get wise to yourself and give up, why don't you do the world a favor and dive off a building? By the end of February, I was registered with twelve agencies and ten of them hadn't produced so much as one courteous word.

But the other two! An ad for "Public Relations Assistant: good media contacts" led me to the first one and to a round little rubber ball of a man who rolled around in his chair as he read my résumé. "Dum de dum de dum," he said. ". . . copy writer . . . de dum de dum . . . account supervisor . . . dum de dum . . . . lots of space buying, I see . . ."

"Good media contacts," I pointed out.

"But not the right ones," he said, rocking back in his chair and spreading a genial smile across me like butter. "Call up an editor and sell him a story, eh? Lots of difference, you know; buying something from their salesman and selling something to their editors."

"But I thought . . ."

" 'Course you did," he said, peering at the second page of the résumé. "Never does any harm to try. Probably handle the job beautifully if they hired you, but they wouldn't, you see. Never mind, you don't want it anyway. Not your line. We'll just have to find something better for you."

I was feeling a bit dazed. "Do you think you can?" I asked.

"We can try, we can try." He held the résumé out at arm's length, and cocked his head on one side, gazing at the pages as if they had been a particularly fine water color. "Good education, good experience; my goodness, yes, we should be able to find something." He rolled forward and raised his finger and I prepared myself for some tidbit of highly confidential information. "What we have to do," he said, "is find the *right* company; somebody who could really use your background. As a matter of fact . . ."

He bounced over to the file cabinet and up-ended himself over the lowest drawer, presenting a vast, spherical bottom to my fascinated gaze. I could hear him dum-de-dumming as he searched through the cards.

"Ah-ha," he said, yanking one out and bobbing upright. "I knew there was something which . . . oh, dear."

"What's the matter?"

"You wouldn't like to go to Chicago, would you?"

"Well, to be honest . . ."

"They'll pay the expenses if they hire somebody here."

"I don't really think so."

"East, west; home's best," he said, tossing the card in a wire basket on top of the cabinet. "That's all we have right at this moment, but there'll be others, there'll be others."

"I hope so," I said with feeling.

"Man with your experience; no trouble finding something. Problem's to find the right thing, eh? We'll try, we'll try."

I left with a good many doubts about *his* effectiveness, but none about my own. I was feeling square-shouldered and iron-jawed, a captain of commerce and a mover of the market-place. If his agency had any success, that could have been its secret; he sent his applicants out robed in confidence.

To do him credit, he *did* try and I had some rather odd adventures as a result. I walked with flawless goddesses through the deep-carpeted corridors of a perfume importing firm to bow before its high priestess ("Sorry, you look good but we need a damn sight more experience in selective marketing"); I breathed in the rich aroma of AT&T Preferred in the oak-paneled office of an investment firm ("I'm Harvard '39; where did you say you went?"); I sat, serene and solemn, among the exuberant, swelling samples of a falsie manufacturer, talking of market patterns and wondering if his secretary had gotten an employee's discount ("Nice to see you but we are—to put it mildly—a pretty specialized business.") I landed none of these jobs and my little round friend never received a fee, though he certainly earned one. I could see why the others preferred to match experience to opening and ignore long shots. The job hunter had to play them, but the agencies didn't, and there was more joy in their accounting department over ten stenographers placed at small fees than there were over ten attempts to place an executive at a large one.

On the ex-oil man's recommendation, I dropped in at another agency, filled out a card, and found myself talking to a man who was obviously an expert in the employment field. He was precise, candid, professional; he had met plenty of displaced white collar workers and he seemed to know their problems. "There's a shortage of executives," he said and he added, with the faintest ghost of a smile, "as I'm sure you've read in the business pages. In some cases, however, when a firm says it can't find a suitable man it means a man just like the one it's trying to replace. Perhaps you've had a run of those. However, your experience is obviously worth something and there has to be a place for you somewhere. I hope we can be the ones to find it."

There was no promise in his statement and the phrase "worth something" was hardly resounding. Nevertheless, I left his office feeling vastly encouraged. In my vulnerable mood, I had the hospital patient's need for assurance that his doctor was competent and interested in his case, and this man seemed to be both. After my first visit, I heard from him at widely spaced but regular intervals —a large corporation on one occasion, a small manufacturing firm on another. These leads, plus the ones furnished by the little round man and the ones which popped up now and then from the more active "executive" employment agencies, plus the ads in the classified section, formed the nucleus of my job-hunting through Febru-

ary. Not all of the leads produced interviews, of course; sometimes
the preliminary telephone call brought a couple of questions and a
curt "Sorry, no point in our seeing you." And some of the leads, I
was amazed to find, could produce more than one interview.

One day the mail brought a polite little note from a firm I had
never heard of: was I still available and could I drop in? I practically plunged in—it was a small chain of variety stores—and spent
a pleasant if fruitless hour with their sales manager. "I figured it
wouldn't do any harm to talk to you," he explained. "You never
know—maybe your old man was in the business or something. But
I couldn't throw you in unless you had *some* experience. Believe
me, I'm doing you a favor." That was that, but I still wondered
where he had obtained my name, and I asked.

"Joe's an old friend of mine," he answered. "You know—Joe,
the under-privileged girl's best friend."

A light dawned—it was the falsie maker.

"Sent me your résumé," the ad manager added, holding it up.
In large letters across the top Joe had scrawled, "Seems like a
good man. Liked him but can't use him. Any help to you?"

Well, as Phil said, you meet all kinds. It probably had taken Joe
one minute to scratch that note and toss the résumé across to his
secretary and it just could have started a lost man on a new career.
Joe was no humanitarian, he just happened to have one minute
more than most people have and that's the stuff of which halos are
made. I offered a small, ribald prayer: may bosoms always stay in
style.

It all added up to two or perhaps three interviews a week, but I
still rode the train in almost every day. The cost was acutely pain-
ful now; handing a dollar through the ticket window was like
pulling a hangnail off and for what? To prowl the train, looking for
familiar faces; to nurse a beer at lunch time under Philippe's contemptuous eye; to sit in the phone booth; to "drop in," at calcu-
lated intervals, to offices where I had long since worn out my welcome; to eat a sandwich at the Automat. Each week I would pick
an absolutely blank day—there would be at least a couple—and
stay home to get "caught up on the paper work." There wasn't
much of it—a letter or two to write, shots in the dark at some remote target; or, perhaps, still another reworking of my résumé. I

was saving the fare, but there was small consolation in that for I was wasting the day. At home, there was not even the remote chance of running into someone "accidentally" and I was acutely conscious of the time ticking away. Perhaps, if I'd gone into the city, this could have been the day. Sometimes I was hit by a hunch so strong that I wanted to jump into the car and drive in—except that Janet had the car and I couldn't drive anyplace.

I hated being at home when Janet returned from her job. Somehow she always managed to walk in the door when I was in a classic shiftless husband pose—lying on the couch, or stealing something out of the refrigerator. She liked her job with Max; it involved a good deal of paper work, but it brought her in contact with an oddly assorted procession of people from the fishermen to elegant young decorators from New York in search of plumbing items which were "not so drearily the same." She began to pick up the jargon of the hardware business and a store of anecdotes. "A man came in today . . ." she would begin brightly and I would find myself setting my teeth. Like every one else in the world, my wife had an identity and I resented it.

I had never realized before just how much information a person picks up through the routine of their job. An ordinary report, a remark dropped by a secretary, a story told over the lunch table—they all had flavored the world in which I had lived and without them I was in exile. Every conversation rammed home my apartness. "How's Hank?" I would ask someone on the train and their eyebrows would rise ever so slightly. "Hank moved on four months ago." Each day my fellow commuters seemed to recede a bit further into their separate world, the world of people who belonged someplace. It was becoming difficult even to talk to them.

I was stepping off the train at Grand Central one morning when Epstein button-holed me and asked with unconscious irony if I were free for lunch. More yacht club stuff, I assumed; with spring coming on he would be rounding up volunteers again. The yacht club was far out of my reach financially now and I didn't give a damn any more. I didn't belong to it or to the country club or even to the community; they were all in another world, too, and I didn't want any part of them. In the restaurant, however, Epstein seemed preoccupied. He talked about boats, but his mind was on something else and finally he brought it out bluntly.

"Still out of work?"

"Well, I've got a couple of things cooking . . ." To hell with it, I was sick of that nonsense. "I'm still out," I answered.

"Rough business," said Epstein. He unwrapped a lump of sugar and dropped it in his coffee. "I was out like that once. Did all my job-hunting from a phone booth in Grand Central. What are you using?"

"Phone booth in Grand Central."

"Could you use an office?"

For some reason the question didn't make sense. "What?" I asked.

"There's a cubicle in our place we aren't using. I hope to move somebody in there eventually, when we can take on more staff, but right now it's empty. You can use it if you want to and the switchboard will handle your calls."

"Well, I . . ."

"Once in a while something comes up with the ad agencies. You know. You could answer a question for us now and then; help out a bit with a problem, maybe. It would be a good deal for us while it lasted. We'd have a stand-by consultant."

"You have no idea how much it would mean to me," I said.

"Okay, we'll move you in after lunch."

On that day the sun chose to shine and we walked to his office in the bright crisp air with our faces turned away from Grand Central. "It isn't much," Epstein warned, guiding me through the door, "but it's bigger than a phone booth." We stopped by the switchboard so I could be introduced to the operator, a pert, black-haired little girl who smiled and said she'd be "happy, I'm sure" to take any messages. The cubicle itself was just around the corner, a tiny, windowless box with one overhead light, a wooden hat-rack, a desk, a chair and a telephone. "Just make yourself at home," said Epstein. "I've got to get back to my own desk and see what the hell is going on." He hurried off down the corridor. I put my attaché case on the desk, hung my hat on the rack, slipped out of my coat and hung that up too and then sat down. As he said, it wasn't much, but its grubby walls enclosed everything I needed so urgently. It was a headquarters, a home, a place to go to and a place to be from, an address and a phone number, a place to sit down and a place to leave things; a location, a destination, an identification.

I was a professional job hunter now, with my own business premises. I might even hang up my shingle on the frosted glass partition:

Job Hunter, Inc.

MARCH

"Big Money for TV Repairmen..."

Sometime around the end of February or the beginning of March I became a professional job hunter. The office had something to do with it, I think; with four frosted glass walls and a desk of my own, I settled into a routine. In the morning I scanned the ads and made the round of agencies ("I'll be back before noon, Miss Harris, in case there are any calls"), in the afternoon I wrote letters, made phone calls and went out for occasional interviews. The tools of my trade were stacked neatly in my desk drawers—shoe-shine kit, spare shirt and necktie, scrapbook and assorted references, and a supply of résumés—four different versions.

The change could be measured in other, more subtle ways; a hardening of attitudes, a certain deftness in handling the job hunter's problems. Only a few months before I had struggled through three drafts of letters and felt crushed when there were no replies. Now they were "mailings"; I fired them off in job lots and considered a ten per cent return to be damn good. I no longer had ideas, merely tactics. I could read between the lines of an ad and I had developed that sixth sense which could separate a hot lead from a cold one or a downright phoney. I had the professional's push and also his wariness; I touched all the bases now, but I wasted very little time. I had learned to classify prospects, reserving the bottom of the list for:

- *Firms that were merely window-shopping for personnel.*
- *Firms that wanted a free consultant. "Why don't you look this over and let us have your ideas, just so we can see what you can do?" Turn in those recommendations and you couldn't get past the switchboard.*
- *Firms which did have an opening, but weren't sure at what level they'd fill it until they saw "who turned up." Almost invariably, they hired a recent college grad.*
- *Firms that wanted a man "who would be one of us." This meant you were trying to join a club, not a company. It also meant, in most cases, that they were trying to find the twin brother of the man they had lost.*
- *Firms which went on interviewing applicants endlessly, unable to make up their minds. 'The job you* do *get," said Les over the lunch table one day, "will probably come through within a week of the initial contact. It stands to reason that if the job's any good, the company will want to fill it as quickly as possible. There could be exceptions, I suppose, but if something drags on more than a week, I kiss it off. That type always dithers until the last possible moment and then grabs the next guy who walks into the office just to fill the vacant chair."*

I became an expert interviewee with techniques for handling the awkward questions which were bound to come up. There was the fencing over "salary expected"—the what-would-you-expect, how-much-were-you-thinking-of-paying circle. This scene had to be underplayed with a confidential smile and a man-to-man tone. Well, salary's a pretty relative thing, isn't it? Depends on the job and the prospects and—just between you and me—the people. Now there's one offer I'm considering which—well, let that go. Let's just say that what a man starts at is less important than what he'll be making in five years' time. The whole question of starting salary is really just a formality; there'll be no problem once I've proved my worth.

|102|

This may sound pretty thin but you have to find some graceful way of asking for what they're offering.

The art of accounting for time:

Beyond a limited number of weeks the mere fact that you're out of a job becomes a barrier to getting one; X won't hire you this week simply because Y didn't last week. You can double the length of your vacation ("Don't often have a chance to get away with the wife and kids") but it isn't wise to stretch it beyond six weeks and it certainly won't cover a year. Illness is out and so is accident; one suggests bad health and the other bad luck—both undesirable qualities. The gap can be filled—somewhat awkwardly—with vague references to unsatisfactory negotiations. ("It seemed like the moment to start my own business, but I spent several months in careful preliminary research and found that the market just wasn't adequate.") An occasional job hunter plugs it with one massive lie—a fictitious trip to Europe perhaps—but this is risky.

The art of editing experience:

". . . of course, a large part of my work *was* production, to all practical purposes. We didn't call it by that name, of course, but most of the situations which would come up in a production job would be pretty familiar to me . . ."

". . . of course, a large part of account work is actually selling. I think it's safe to say that anyone who'd held down such a job has all the attributes of a good salesman . . ."

I acquired the ability to absorb humiliation and I learned, as Phil had warned I would learn, that the nice guys may not be so nice when you are merely one more homeless human. I absorbed the application forms and their curt demands for information which I usually never gave to anyone outside my family. I filled them out because I had to, and I learned from them that human dignity is something more than a four-color spread of a sunset and a quote from John Stuart Mill. Its essential element is privacy of your home and your family affairs, of your person and your thoughts; that privacy which permits the little legends which help us live with ourselves and each other. The forms (check one) left room for no little legends; they opened out my soul like the front of a doll's house.

I absorbed the psychological tests. I took them because I had to, and I learned from them that the man who asks the questions can dictate the answers. I was afraid the tests would bar me from a job for which I was qualified, and equally afraid that they would get me hired for the wrong reasons, placing me among people who had been led to expect something I had never promised.

I absorbed the curt turndowns and the cold little printed slips and the smug voices of secretaries and the contemptuous stares of "junior executives." I even absorbed the grim, funny little ironies. _____, bless his affluent old heart, took me to lunch at the Yale Club and solemnly presented me with a yellowed brochure entitled "Selling yourself." Its opening sentence: "As you leave college to enter the world of business . . ." And then there was that phone call from an outfit which had simply ignored all my letters. Did I know young Mr. So-and-so? I did, since I had hired and trained him some years in the past and I had a high opinion of him. "That's fine," said the hearty voice on the other end of the line. "We're glad to have your recommendation. I guess we'll hire him." And, finally, there was a heartbreaker: "We thought of you for this spot we had, but we couldn't pay what you were getting and we figured you wouldn't be interested . . ."

"Have you tried running an ad?" Epstein asked one day. I had thought of it some months before, an austere ad in a business publication, perhaps, or a few dignified paragraphs surrounded by plenty of white space in the financial section of the Sunday paper. It had seemed silly, however, if something was bound to break at any moment, and I had been held back, too, by a certain self-consciousness. I hadn't become résumé-hardened in those days and I felt the smart boys would spot me hiding behind the box number and sneer at my description of my own talents. Now I didn't give a damn. I had the brassiness all right; what I didn't have was the budget. If I bought any advertising space it would have to be a few lines in the "Positions Wanted" column.

Impulsive decisions can be a mixed blessing. If the job hunter doesn't take a plunge now and then he doesn't make anything move; if he does, he has to push the cost out of his mind and this can be dangerous. I tossed it back and forth—hot one day and cold the next—and then suddenly decided what-the-hell and began pecking at my portable:

"A CHALLENGE! Can your company keep up with a man of ideas, an executive who . . ."

Nope.

"DON'T ANSWER THIS AD—if aggressive thinking bothers you and ideas are not in your line . . ."

Oh, God.

"ARE YOU LOOKING FOR—a planner who works in the present and thinks in the future, who doesn't let limits on budget put limits on imagination . . ."

At this point I pushed back the chair and walked around the room a couple of times and did some thinking. The eye-catching head was great—if you had some space to support it. In a few lines of tiny type, it seemed to me, it might just look silly. It also ran up the linage at a terrific rate and, in any event, I wasn't quite sure that the hot-shot image was the one I wanted to project. I went back to the typewriter and roughed out a couple of versions of a simple, informative ad. It looked a lot better to my eye—more intelligent and more businesslike—but it brought up another problem: the words which meant "experienced" were likely to carry overtones of "middle-aged."

The final version:

MARKETING EXPERT - ~~senior~~ seasoned marketing and advertising executive with ~~lengthy~~ comprehensive creative and management background. ~~Well-versed thoroughly and originate~~ Has originated ad ideas and marketing programs and ~~implemented~~ directed product promotions.

"Is that all?" asked Janet.

"That's all."

"It doesn't say very much," she said doubtfully. "What is 'management background?' "

"Oh, making decisions and planning and so on. If you want the truth," I added bitterly, "any man who spent one week in the ad business and couldn't come up with better copy than that ought to be shot. The trouble is that I want to keep it as vague as possible because the moment I get specific I lose a hundred possible leads. It's too specific as it is, but I can't help that and I can't think of anything better."

I browsed through the "Situations Wanted" column to see what other men did with their half-inch or so of space. Some of the ads were terse and factual, reflecting a confidence that a good record *must* speak for itself; others tried to pack a breezy bounciness into four lines of tiny type. "ORGANIZATION MAN," said one ad proudly, still hymning the loyalty which had proved to be a one-way street. "CAN YOU KEEP UP WITH A REAL IDEA MAN?" asked another, echoing some of my own discarded efforts. There was a runaway inflation of personal adjectives—"dynamic," "industrious," "imaginative," "resourceful"—and a dozen different efforts to divorce experience from the implication of age—"youthfully mature"; "young-minded"; and my own evasion, "seasoned." Some of the ads were chilling. "My God," I thought, looking at one, "if a guy that good can't find any takers, what chance have I got?"

I turned my own effort over to the newspaper with no real anticipation and when Sunday rolled around I opened the classified section to see how it looked in print.

It took me five minutes to find it.

I let Monday and Tuesday slide by and checked at the newspaper office on Wednesday, braced for the word "nothing." The clerk reached into the box and pulled out a handful of envelopes. One, two, three, four, five, six, seven envelopes!

"Keep-counter-clear-please," said the clerk. "Next."

I dropped them into my attaché case and walked back to the office, trying to maintain a professional calm.

"Got sumpin'?" asked Epstein's switchboard operator.

"Maybe," I said. I hung my hat up in the cubicle, sat down behind the desk and began opening the replies.

Religious tract.

Book brochure: "How I Sold My Way To Success In Six Months."

Form letter, recruiting door-to-door salesmen.

Religious tract.

Correspondence course brochure: "Big Money If You Become A TV REPAIRMAN!"

Letter and booklet: "Have you ever considered the advantages and EXTRA INCOME to be gained from operating a business RIGHT IN YOUR OWN HOME?..."

A precise and uncommunicative letter requesting a résumé and "details of salary expected" from Somebody Associates of Some-where, New Jersey. I read it twice and then re-examined the en-velope; neither the letterhead nor the single, crisp paragraph gave any clue to the nature of the opening—if there was one—or of Somebody Associates' business. I showed the letter to Epstein's secretary, who shook her head.

"Never heard of them," she said, "but they might be listed in one of the directories." They weren't, however, so I finally shrugged and mailed off a résumé with a brief covering note which made no mention of "salary expected."

That was the end of my advertising campaign. "You know," I told Janet, "I think I'll resign this account."

The important thing—the biggest thing of all—was to avoid thinking. To plan, of course; to work and to dig, to write letters, to make phone calls, to check the ads and follow up the leads, to push here and duck there and project that youthful maturity at in-terviews, to spend the dollar and save the penny and say hiyah to the neighbors and something's-in-the-works to the boys on the train and do what you could for the kids and work with the wife on the budget and even to worry about the bills and the bank account but above everything else, to avoid thinking.

If you think, you panic.

It's not so bad during the day, you can concentrate on schemes or even on problems if the problems are things of the moment—what should I say in this letter or how will I handle this guy tomor-row? It's the night moments which are bad, the moments which come when you're lying in bed and the thinking starts and the whole business begins to drift together into a pattern. It goes on like this, and on and on, week after week, month after month, and there's no measurement of time except the dwindling of the bank account and the dwindling of our lives. Days are dollars; dollars are days. A year ago we had six months, and we learned how to cut back a nickel here and a dime there and we stretched it. Then we yanked the kids out of everything and clamped down hard on the budget and sold the car and added Janet's salary and we stretched it again and yet again, thinner and thinner, past any point that was possible and past that again, pushing the ultimate day of disaster into the future but still creeping toward it, day by relent-less day. What happened when it all ran out; the dollars and then the dimes and then the credit and then even the charity? So my mind ran on to the point of a physical agony which pulled me bolt upright in bed.

But it doesn't help, of course; it doesn't help one damn bit to brood like that. The thing to do is lie down and get some sleep, to quit borrowing trouble, to worry about the next day if you must worry about something.

Or to grope around for the slippers and find the flashlight and go down to the kitchen for a cup of coffee, to sit at the metal-topped table with the blueberry stain which never quite came out of the enamel and wonder why the thing that each man fears always creeps up in the dark.

Perhaps your wife awakens, as Janet did one night, and comes downstairs quietly to pour the coffee out and sit across the table, wanting to help but wondering what words could drive away demons.

"Don't worry about it," I told her. "It's stupid. I'm too old to be scared of the dark."

"No, you're not. Nobody is."

"It's just that it sneaks up. I lie there in bed and there's nothing else to do or think about and it just sort of . . . sneaks up. It's like being bitten by a snake."

"Why didn't you wake me up?" she asked.

"Because you need your sleep. And because it's stupid."

She reached across the table and took my hand. "No, it isn't," she said. "And even if it was, that wouldn't make any difference. You've been explaining yourself to people for so long you've forgotten something—you don't have to explain yourself to me. All you have to say is 'it hurts.' That's all I need to know."

"You've got your problems," I said. "I don't want to add to them."

"It's not a question of problems. Problems you can carry alone; fears like this you can't. Everyone's scared when they're alone in a haunted house, I don't care what they say. You shouldn't be ashamed to yell for help, not with me. With other people, maybe, but not with me."

Things were better now with the lights on and the coffee in front of me and Janet standing by. It came to me suddenly that my concern for her might have gone too far and become something wounding.

"If I keep anything from you," I said, "it may be because I'm keeping it from myself. There are some things . . . Well, they may never happen. I know they're creeping closer, but if something broke—tomorrow, maybe; next week—they'd never have to be faced. But then if I'm lying in bed in a dark room, something like a little film starts running through my head and I can see things happening . . ."

"What sort of things?"

"Oh . . . the house, the mortgage. If you sit down in broad daylight and talk about foreclosures and people being thrown out into the snow it all sounds sort of melodramatic. But it *could* happen, you know; it just could happen. Sometimes, this hour of the morning, I can see it happening."

It was my plantation I was talking about, the home of our children and the fruit of our growth in the world, and it was a strange thing to face the fact that most of it really belonged to somebody else.

"Okay," said Janet, "that's a practical problem and we can talk about it practically."

"Well, practically, we just can't carry it much longer. The more I think about it, the more I think we've carried it too long as it is."

"Then that's that. The question is where do we go from here?"

"That's what we have to decide. Up to now, I've more or less gone on the basis that we didn't want to relocate. I figured the question would settle itself. If something really terrific came up— something so good I'd be crazy to turn it down—then it would obviously pay us to pull up stakes. Otherwise, no. Now, I guess you could say that if we have to move twenty miles we may as well move two hundred. Or two thousand."

"We don't have to decide right now about relocating, do we? I mean, if something turns up, we could decide then, couldn't we?"

"I think we ought to decide in principle," I said. "Look at it this way. Suppose there's some outfit which has an opening in—oh, Houston. I think I ought to know before I go in for the interview whether we're willing to make such a move or not."

This was a damn serious problem and I had been stewing about

|109|

it, off and on, ever since the little round man in the employment agency had mentioned Chicago.

"If I do take some job in Houston or what have you, I'm getting off base. If it works out, fine; if it doesn't, we'd have to find our way back to New York somehow because we don't know anyone there and besides"—this was the key point—" there are only so many jobs I *could* get in Houston or Cleveland or Denver. New York, now—San Francisco, maybe—I could keep on turning up possibilities forever. . . ."

"Well, then . . ."

"Wait a minute, let me finish. On the other hand, so far as the house goes, I'm in favor of dumping it anyway. Let's put it on the market Monday. That's what I think."

Janet got up and walked over to the window, the one which looked out on the patio, and began fiddling with the latch.

"I guess that answers it," she said.

"Answers what?"

"Well, we can hang on to the house if we want to. I mean, there's a way if we really want to hang on to it."

"How, for God's sake?"

"Borrow the money from Melly."

"I . . ."

"He'd let us have it, you know that." Janet was speaking very quickly. "Melly would lend somebody the money to save their home because you know how he is about that and people's homes and the kids and their having roots. If he knew we were thinking of selling the place he'd insist on lending us the money. He *will* insist when he finds out."

"No," I said. And I stopped right there, wondering how to put the rest of it. The charge against me was cruelty, not toward the four walls but toward the values they had enclosed and I wanted to say that we'd take these things with us, the love and the laughter and the tin-topped table with the blueberry stain on the enamel. It had been our home and as a home I loved every foot of green lumber in its walls and every crack in the cheap concrete and every inch of water which seeped into the basement and every draft which whistled through the windows and even the gravel in what was supposed to be the garden and the soft loam in what was supposed to be the driveway. As a home I loved it but as a house it was nothing but a split-level egg-crate and we didn't fit it any more. We had bought it, and its location, to prove we had "arrived," but now we had departed and the house was like the memory of an indiscretion.

"It depends on how you feel," I said. "If you really . . ."

"Don't throw it in *my* lap," she answered. "If we've got to move, we've got to and that's it."

"I'm not throwing it in your lap; I'm trying to find out what you think about it. I didn't know you had any old family homestead feelings about this place; if you have, then we'll try to hang on. If it's really important to you—*really* important—I'll go to Melly and hit him up for the money."

"I wouldn't make you do that and you know I wouldn't. If we had to hit up Melly—and I hope to God we never have to—I'd do it. He's my brother and I guess that makes him my responsibility. It's not important anyway because I haven't got any old homestead feelings. I'm just worried about a couple of things."

"Such as?"

"Well—where do we go from here and what about the kids . . . security and roots and that sort of thing?"

"We find some place we can rent cheaply for the time being until we know where we're headed. The kids . . . well, we can probably stick it out until the end of the school year. If we did find a buyer before then, we could fix things up somehow. Perhaps somebody could put them up, just for a few weeks, like . . . like . . ."

"Go on, say it."

"Like Melly and Marge," I said, unhappily. "There's no escape."

"I wasn't talking about the school," said Janet. "We can straighten that out. What I meant was that they . . . we . . . ought to have a home someplace. Not here, maybe; I'll go along with that. There isn't anything for us here, I can see that. We bought a house that was built on sand and we may as well face it. We'll leave some friends behind—Max and a couple of others—but outside of that I don't think we'll be losing a damn thing. But there's got to be *someplace* that *is* home; someplace that *does* have something for us. There's got to be someplace where you go on being

|111|

part of the community even if you're out of work for a few months; the whole Goddam world can't be one big Disneyland."

"Of course it isn't," I told her. "The world's still round and the United States of America is out there someplace. We'll just have to keep sailing until we find it."

I didn't know what to think about the kids and the possible effects of uprooting them. That was a problem I had been shoving off on Janet. I had to do this, but I may as well admit I was relieved to have an excuse for ducking the headaches. There had been plenty of them.

I knew Janet was thinking mainly of young Skip; we'd made a bad mistake there and we hadn't realized it in time. Cliff kicked up most of the fuss and got most of the attention; Skip seemed to accept the situation quietly and we had assumed that most of it was beyond his grasp. He had asked questions now and then, small probing questions which should have been a tip-off.

"Are we going to have a tree next Christmas?" This came quite suddenly one mid-January evening and I said, "Sure we are, why not?"

"Am I going back to the same school next year?" I was plowing through some letters at that moment and I answered "Yup." He hung around for a moment as if he had something else to ask—I remembered this later—and then he wandered away.

"Are we going to have only one car always?"; "How much does electricity cost?"; "When is Cliff going to get his boat?" Ordinary questions; some of them a bit young for his age, perhaps, but nothing to get alarmed about, especially since he always seemed satisfied with the answers. If you put them all together, however, you could see what he was trying to find out and what was going on in his mind.

If we could retain one memory from childhood it ought to be the knowledge of just how many things a child sees and hears and how likely he is to put his own meanings into them. There were certain things which helped me keep a sense of proportion—a lunch with Phil, an encouraging word from Epstein, a talk with one of the more capable employment agencies—but these things weren't passed on to the kid and the smell of fear was. Skip was feeling every bruise I felt and he hadn't any liniment to put on any of them.

He became quiet—too quiet. His school work started to slip badly and he stood on the sidelines during sports periods and then the night creatures began reaching out of the dark corners for him, too. There was the night Janet passed his door and heard him crying and we both sat up for a couple of hours coaxing as many of his fears out of him as we could. He was sure we were going to move—that part was accurate enough—and he had built a terrifying picture of the place we might move to, part fact, part impressions of the outside world picked up from television and things other kids had told him at school. There it was and there wasn't a damn thing we could do about it; he had drifted into this through the months, adding one impression to another, and he'd have to be pulled out of it the same way. No one reassurance could do it. We had to listen to his questions and try to work out what he was really asking and answer that. It helped a little, but not very much.

But Skip, at least, was still part of the family.

I wasn't so sure about Cliff. He stayed away from the house as much as possible, cadging meals at the homes of schoolmates and rides from their parents. He seemed to view his own home with only two emotions, contempt and resentment. I could look at Skip's face and see the baby which was still there; when I looked into Cliff's eyes in off-guard moments I could sense a cold, calculating adult and something beyond even that, something primitive and frightening. Perhaps it was my imagination, rubbed raw by friction with the kids, but I could feel the force of some elemental pressure, an animal instinct to survive and to attack which was not to be turned aside by any human values. At such moments he was not Cliff nor was he anyone I had ever known; he was a citizen of some strange, brutal world yet to come, waiting until he could smash us and the silly, fragile things we valued with a few casual kicks and enter into his true heritage.

I said nothing about this to Janet, beyond agreeing that Cliff was "developing into a problem." Privately, I had a growing suspicion that our problems weren't his and our future held nothing he wanted any part of. Whether we moved or stayed, I was sure, made very little difference to him; it was all temporary in any event and wherever we might go, he would find his way to his own grim destination from there.

What was it all about, anyway; where did it all come from? My father had moved from Ohio when I was twelve and homes were hardly secure in those depression days. I could remember the strange, bleak look of the house after the furniture had been crated, the empty rooms which were suddenly smaller, the square and oval patches on the wall where the pictures had hung. I could remember pushing aside the broken lattice and crawling under the porch to my hideaway to get my cap pistol and to bury forever the illegal candle and box of matches. I could remember walking across the meadow for a last look at the pond, a last look which meant nothing because "never again" was a phrase I still couldn't grasp. I could remember—in a series of blurred snapshots—the train trip which seemed to go on forever and the lights of strange cities whipping by in the night. I could remember the first real pain, which came only when we walked into the new house; the cold, hostile new house with no meadow, no pond and no porch at all. I had clung tightly to the cap pistol for it was a formidable weapon which had kept all the forces of evil at bay and could destroy the whole town if necessary. But with all of this there had been a sense of adventure, too; new places to explore and new people who talked about new things. In time, the cap pistol was pushed to the rear of the dresser drawer and forgotten. Perhaps my sense of security was shaken, but that may not have been a bad thing. "For God's sake," I said, brooding about it on the train one morning, "they used to send kids to sea at thirteen."

And then, on the second day of April, Epstein walked into my office with a handful of papers.

"You Are Welcome to Sue Us If You Wish"

It was a thin sheaf of papers; a couple of magazine pages, one typewritten sheet, a few columns clipped from newspapers. Epstein dropped them on the desk. "These come from one of my esteemed clients," he said. "It represents their total advertising effort for the year."

"What are they selling?" I asked. "Thumbtacks?"

"Take a look and tell me what you think."

I spread the ads out and examined them. The copy was drab and overcrowded, it was a cinch to sink into the page without leaving a ripple. It was all amateurish and it was all pretty awful.

"Who's their agency?"

"Are you kidding?" said Epstein pointing to the typewritten sheet. "With that budget? This is strictly do-it-yourself."

"Well, it stinks."

"That's what I told them." Epstein sat down in the straight chair, the only other chair in the cubicle. "Diplomatically, of course. I also told them that if they weren't willing to quadruple that budget and line up an agency, they should at least call in a pro. I said I knew a good one who just happened to be available if they grabbed quick. So what do you think?"

"Well, I could certainly iron out that copy. But if they're that broke or that tight-fisted . . ." I was balancing the equation; a few welcome dollars against the investment of time.

"It isn't that simple," said Epstein. "Let's see if I can give you the picture. These are damn smart production people. They'll trade in a machine if the paint starts to chip off it, and they could tell you down to the last penny just how much it costs them to turn out a single unit. They've got a good name, or they *did* have. The momentum's wearing off now and the competition is making some hefty inroads. The trouble with these people is that every time they think about the problem they slide back into the same groove and start talking about production efficiency. If you say 'advertising' they say yes, of course, that's important too and they'll get around to it just as soon as they can."

Epstein leaned across the desk and tapped the clippings. "The point is," he continued, "that they need something more than a little copywriting. They need reorientation. They need someone who's half adman and half psychologist. I told them they should have a consultant."

"I'm not a psychologist," I objected. "I can come up with some ideas but if they don't see the obvious necessity for. . . ."

"It's not obvious to *them*," said Epstein emphatically, tapping on the desk again. "That's ninety per cent of the job, you see; that's where you'd really earn your money. The problem isn't the copy, it's the attitude the copy reflects. Lick that and the rest would be downhill . . ."

"Well, I . . ."

"You don't have to decide this minute," said Epstein, standing up. "Think it over and let me know next week."

I bounced the idea off Janet.

"Grab it," she said. "Grab it and charge them a whopping fee."

"I don't know, I hate this idea of temporary work. It means we stay even for a few weeks and then I'm out in the street again and we're back where we started. At the best we'd get ahead of the game by a few bucks and what does that mean? A couple of weeks—three or four at the most. Meanwhile, some damn good lead could pop up and I'd lose out on it."

Janet held up one finger. "First, the chances are that no damn good lead will pop up. Second . . ." she held up another finger ". . . it wouldn't necessarily hurt your chances if you were handling a consulting job for a good firm, even if it is a smallish one. If you charged them enough you could get more than a couple of weeks ahead of the game."

"I can't hit them up for a fat fee just because *we* need the dough. I've got to charge what the job's worth. If I were one of these experts . . ."

"You *are* an expert," said Janet, "you just don't think like one, that's all. Something takes you ten minutes and it's routine stuff so you're going to say this is on the house boys, glad to help out. Or you're going to charge them one dollar and feel all squirmy when you take the money."

"So what would you do?"

"Charge them plenty," she said promptly, "and let 'em know they're lucky to get you. Because they *are,* that's what you have to see. They might have spent ten *days* trying to find the answer for themselves; they might have shot ten times as much as you'd charge, then pulled some expensive boner on top of it. Where do you think *our* money goes? You paid a television man fifteen bucks just to pull one tube out of the set and put another one in. That took him less than *five* minutes and it was routine stuff to *him,* you can bet on that. These people of Epstein's are floundering around; they don't know where to begin. The very smallest part of what you know might save them a mint. Isn't that worth something? Besides, you know you'll work like a ditchdigger on it and that ought to be worth something too."

The weekend went by before I had a chance to consult anyone else, but the following Tuesday I ran into Les and the oilman at the Automat.

"Grab it," said Les.

"And rack up a big, juicy fee," added the oilman.

I spread out my doubts like a grimy tablecloth.

"Okay," said the oilman, taking out a pen and pointing it at me. "Let's begin at the beginning. In the first place, you're thinking of this as so many dollars for so much work—probably at more or less the level you used to make. Right?"

"Well . . . I guess so."

"But it isn't that sort of job. The amount of work isn't important; what counts is whether they get what they want or not. What they *really* want, I mean."

|117|

I must have looked puzzled, because the oilman looked at Les and laughed.

"Let me give you an example," he said. "A company has a problem. They call in an expert—that's you. Any work you can do, any advice you can give, may be useful of course, but the chances are it will all lead to the same conclusion they've already reached. And *that's* when you earn your money."

"For what?"

"Making up their minds for them. Backing up their own opinions. Giving them an out, so they can say they were following expert advice and not just making a snap judgment."

"There's a couple of other possibilities," Les added. "They may want you to do something which is better done by an outsider. Reorganizing channels, perhaps—they could do it themselves, but that might mean feuds or resentments within the company. So they call you in and pay you to be hated. Ditto for anything which might involve firing somebody, of course."

"Have either of you ever done anything of this sort?" I asked.

"I have," said the oilman. "Twice. One of them was a straight consulting job. You want to remember that there are firms who need services once in a while, but not often enough to set up a permanent department. Sometimes you can turn them into a regular customer or even set things up on a retainer basis. The other was a big organization, all protocol and channels and departments within departments and so on. Nobody could move unless somebody else moved first and when they needed something done in a hurry, they called in an outsider. *He* could move without upsetting the system. I soaked them for plenty."

"Because they were big?"

"No," said the oilman dryly, "because I charge more for being a messenger boy."

And, finally, at the end of the week, I went back to Epstein.

"First," he said, "I agree with Janet. If I didn't think you could do a job for these people I wouldn't have recommended you. They're *my* clients, remember, and I figure I'm doing them a favor. Second, your friends may have overstated the case a little, but they made some good points. Getting the job done may involve . . uh . . adjusting a few attitudes."

"How much should I charge them?"

"Whatever is right for the job. Don't overcharge them and don't undercharge them."

"But what *is* right?" I asked somewhat desperately. "Ten dollars, a million dollars? What's usual?"

"That depends," said Epstein. "You have to figure what your time is worth, for a start. Then you have to figure what your knowledge is worth and don't undervalue that. It took you a good many years and a lot of work to gain it and it's worth something. Finally you have to charge enough to cover yourself—call it a certain premium for your availability. They are taking you out of circulation for the duration of this job and you might just miss out on something else."

"I don't think that's too likely."

"You don't know whether it is or not; it could be. The point is that you have to charge them enough so you can afford to do a good job for them. You aren't doing them any favor by cutting your price to the bone; you could save them a few bucks and cause them to lose a lot. Also, to be honest about it, they won't value anything they get too cheap. If somebody offered you a new car for a hundred bucks, the first thing you'd say would be 'What's wrong with it?' Figure out a good price and then look the job over and slide it up or down a bit, depending on what you see. Now, the question is: do you want to tackle it?"

"Okay," I decided, impulsively.

"Okay," said Epstein. "And just remember one thing—you're the expert."

It was a noble thought and it propped up my confidence for an additional week until I actually made an appointment and arrived at the door of their office building. The building was bigger than I had expected and that rattled me. The lobby rattled me, too, and so did the receptionist; both were neat, cool, precise. "Ah, yes," she said. "You're the Ten O'clock Meeting." She reached for the intercom. Click, buzz. "Mr. Gilbrick's Ten O'clock Meeting is here," she announced.

What the hell was this lump in my gut? I had recommended campaigns for companies vastly bigger than this one—yes, and fought down their objections. But I was armored then; I carried a title like a banner and the resounding, many-commaed name of a major agency went before me with the sound of trumpets.

|119|

Mr. Gilbrick's secretary arrived and identified me as the Ten O'clock Meeting. "If you'd just come with me," she said. "They're waiting for you in the conference room." This was ominous; I had hoped for an informal, preliminary meeting and a chance to sound them out. Apparently I'd be facing a jury and a short-order verdict. Down one long corridor, around the corner, through the paneled door and there was the conference room. Heavy drapes, more paneling, long table, leather chairs, one portrait—probably Our Founder—and one cut-away drawing of machinery.

And there was Mr. Gilbrick, gray battleship steel upholstered in tweed.

"Good morning ah . . . this is Mr. Endicot, our production manager . . ."

Square cast-iron in a blue shirt with a detachable collar.

". . . Mr. Heath, our treasurer . . ."

Smooth, white marble in depression blue.

". . . Mr. Gilbrick, Junior, my administrative assistant . . ."

Six feet of uncertainty.

". . and Mr. Lewis, our executive director."

Cold, brittle glass in soft gray flannel.

"Shall we get started?"

Mr. Gilbrick sat down and folded his hands. Mr. Endicot sat down and pulled out a large cigar. Mr. Heath sat down, laid a notebook on the table and a gold pen beside it. Mr. Gilbrick, Junior, sat down, lit a cigarette and promptly stubbed it out. Mr. Lewis sat down and produced a slim, polished pipe.

I sat down and they all stared at me expectantly.

"Well," I said, "I . . uh . . understand you're having some trouble with . . . ah . . . there's some question about your advertising."

A genial smile, sudden and startling, swept over Mr. Gilbrick's face. I had a hunch that it was dreaded in that building more than anyone else's frown.

"Mr. Epstein seems to think so," he said.

"I do *not* think so," said Mr. Heath. He picked up his gold pen and laid it on top of the notebook. Mr. Lewis removed his pipe from his mouth and blew a cloud of smoke at the ceiling. "Possibly," he said.

"Endicot?"

"I'd like to hear what this gentleman has to say."

Mr. Gilbrick's smile broadened. He looked at Gilbrick, Junior.

"You know what I think," muttered Gilbrick, Junior.

"My son takes much the same view as Mr. Epstein," said Mr. Gilbrick. "May I ask if you've seen any of our advertising?"

This was beginning to get on my nerves. The session was off to a bad start and I had a feeling they were probing for something. Then, between one breath and the next, I saw what the boys at the Automat had been trying to tell me. These people would know an agency by reputation, but they didn't know me and they were trying to sound out my status. Philosopher or mechanic? Doctor or repairman? Policy-maker or bolt-tightener? It all hung on my next few words; if they were too tough or too mild they could kill the job.

I could do that job, that was the main point. Lewis couldn't; his pipe and his gray flannel seemed to be all he had and they weren't enough. Heath couldn't; he knew why things shouldn't be done, but not why they should. Endicot had the guts but he didn't have the ideas; Junior had ideas but he didn't have the guts. That left Gilbrick, and I could see right through that armorplate and tweed; things were getting out of control and Gilbrick was scared. They were looking for a miracle, not a man; they wanted a pill to make the pain go away.

"Yes," I said, "I've seen your stuff and I'd be happy to give you a recommendation."

"Just a moment," Heath interrupted. "I think we should discuss some arrangement . . ."

"That's okay. This is a very simple recommendation and there'll be no charge."

"What is it?" asked Gilbrick. He was still smiling.

"Quit advertising."

The smile vanished abruptly.

"Cancel your schedule," I added. "Pull all your ads out. Put the money someplace else."

In the silence which followed, there was enough time for me to rummage in my pockets for a cigarette and light it. At the end of the table, Endicot began to wheeze like an air compressor. His cheeks grew puffy, his forehead turned red. He tossed his cigar in the ashtray, put both hands on the tabletop and guffawed. "Terrific," he said, "just terrific."

"I suppose you're joking . . ." Gilbrick began uncertainly.

"Of course he isn't," said Endicot. "He's perfectly serious. You are perfectly serious, aren't you?"

"Yes, I am," I said. I had guessed right about the production manager's guts, but I had underestimated his imagination. Gilbrick still hadn't grasped the point but his smile was pasted back on. "Perhaps," he said, "you gentlemen can let me in on this joke which is so serious."

"Go on," said Junior suddenly. "Tell him."

I put my attaché case on the table, snapped it open and took out their ads. I stood up so I could spread the copy across the table and remained standing while I delivered my explanation. I made it short and candid:

"These aren't ads, they're announcements. All they say is that you exist and you're willing to do business with anyone who gets in touch with you . . ."

"We've got a damn good sales force . . ." Lewis said, pointing the stem of his pipe at me.

"Oh, let him finish," said Endicot.

"A damn good sales force needs damn good support," I said. I had a hunch that Lewis' title of "executive director" might include copywriting, but it was too late to turn back now. "I don't think these are supplying it. Apart from the ads themselves—we can go into details about them later—there's no relationship between them, no continuity, no theme. To all practical purposes, you have no advertising program at all and that's why I suggest that you make it official and just quit buying space."

I sat down.

Lewis pointed his pipe at me again, but Heath beat him to the punch.

"I knew we'd get to this," said the treasurer grimly. "More money, that's what it boils down to; the sum total of your expert advice is that we should spend more money."

"As a matter of fact," I pointed out, "I just suggested that you spend less. These ads represent waste, Mr. Heath; you can eliminate it. Whether you actually do spend less or whether you spend more is something for you to decide. I wouldn't presume to advise you on that. The sum total of my expert advice is that you can't mount an adequate advertising campaign on what you're spending now—not these days. If you do decide to increase your budget I can see that you *spend* it, not waste it."

Lewis finally got his word in.

"You'd also want to . . ah . . hype up the ads, if that's the correct Madison Avenue expression."

"You could call it that," I answered briefly. I wasn't going to get sidetracked into a fencing match with him.

"How much do you think we would have to increase our budget?" asked Gilbrick.

"I don't know exactly; I'd have to study your situation. I think it's safe to say it would be a substantial amount."

"As our consultant," Gilbrick added, "we would expect you to find ways to reduce this cost, ways to cut corners."

Epstein hadn't been kidding when he said they need reorientation.

"As your consultant," I said, "I would *not* find ways to cut corners. That would land you right back where you are now. I would find ways to make every dollar you spend do a job for you. This is a battle and I wouldn't be competent if I let you walk into it with a pea-shooter. I may as well tell you right now that one of the major things I would hope to do is help you line up an agency."

"If we're—ah—upping our budget," said Gilbrick, "assuming we do, of course; I mean if we do—why couldn't we just go straight to an agency? What could you do for us that they couldn't?"

"Not a damn thing," I answered. "They could do it better, in fact; they've got the staff and equipment. They also have other clients to worry about, clients with their own problems. Now if you can work with an agency, if you can give them positive decisions and some idea of where you're heading, then you should go directly to one."

I waited for another long moment while each man tested the reality of that phrase "positive decisions" in his own mind. It was Endicot, again, who spoke first.

"How much time do you think you'd need?"

|123|

"Probably a month, possibly five weeks?"

"What about your fee?" snapped Heath.

I still hadn't worked it out; the figure just popped into my mind.

"Two thousand dollars," I said.

Gilbrick's smile remained fixed. Lewis examined the bowl of his pipe. Heath stared at the wall. I sensed that the moment had come.

"If there are no more questions," I added standing up. "I have a lunch appointment . . ."

Gilbrick jumped to his feet, pumped my hand and opened the door.

"It was a pleasure to make your acquaintance," I finished. "Thank you for your time and attention."

I closed the door behind me and, as I turned the corner into the corridor, the voices began. It sounded as if they were all talking at once but, beyond the others, I could hear Endicot's boom and Heath's dry, flat snarl . .

There was a certain irony in the whole business. If I had impressed them at all, it was because I'd been talking to a man I knew better than anyone else, I'd been talking to my sometime self. Gilbrick with his good guy smile, that had been me; Heath's bullying, Lewis' posing, Junior's sulking, they'd all been pieces of a thing that once called himself "an executive."

"How did it go?" Epstein asked when I returned to the office and I said "Damned if I know." I was damned if I did; I had no yardsticks for measuring that sort of interview and I wasn't going to sweat about it. There were two telephone messages waiting for me and I had work to do.

One message was from a statistical analysis firm—they wanted a vaguely defined "administrative executive." The other, from a suburban manufacturer, was an unexpected return from one of my mailings. I called the manufacturer first and set up a date for the following Wednesday. Then—somewhat puzzled—I phoned the statistical firm, explained myself to a secretary and again to Mr. Whatzit's own personal executive secretary and won an audience for Monday. This meant I'd be out of the office for a day and a half in the following week and I wasn't going to sweat about that, either. If Gilbrick and his merry men weren't interested I'd never hear from them again; if they were, assuming I hadn't heard from them already, it wouldn't hurt matters any if I was hard to reach.

I went to the Automat for lunch.

"It sounds like you ought to have a chance," said Les. "At least they didn't heave you out on your ear. That was smart, by the way; ending the interview yourself. You quit while you were winning. Now let's see if we can guess who'll call if they do want you."

"Well, the old man, I guess—Gilbrick."

Les shook his head. "Right now—assuming they've decided to go ahead with it—they're sitting around arguing about which one of them can do the best job of handling you. Gilwhoozit will stay out of the whole business—I'm so sure of that I'll bet a cream cheese and pimento sandwich on it. There's got to be somebody who stays remote so he can be the final court of appeal if any deadlocks develop. It won't be the production guy—it isn't his department—and they obviously won't trust Junior with it, so it has to be the treasurer or the gray flannel jerk . . ."

"Lewis."

"Yeah, him. You sort of left him in a one-down position and I know that type. God knows *you* ought to. He's got to end up superior to you if he's going to stay equal with himself, so I'll make a bet he volunteers for the job. Keep an eye on him if you should go over there."

I finished my sandwich and walked over to the Public Library where I spent the afternoon looking up the two companies which would be interviewing me. The next morning, I went straight from the station to a second-hand magazine shop which carried back issues of trade and technical magazines. A company's ads, especially the ones it aims at the trade, can tell you a lot about its goals and its problems. Some firms have hell's own time enlisting distributors, for example. If the ads harp on high mark-ups or claim the consumer advertising is creating the greatest demand in history, it's a good bet the company is bucking this headache. Or, again, one loaf of bread is pretty much like another and the guy that bakes it has to find some difference which will catch the consumer's eye. If the ads emphasize packaging or quick delivery service or the special, secret ingredient they're a tip-off that you're walking into a highly competitive business. Beyond all this, the advertising can give you a clue to the company's outlook and the face you should wear at the interview. It's a mistake to assume that a dignified ad means a dignified company; these days it *can* mean that they've stepped up their image-building because they've let the quality of their product slip. And not every whimsical ad reflects a sense of humor. The firm's agency may have talked the management into it or they may simply be trying to copy a more successful competitor. What I looked for was the tone of the ads, the feel of the copy, the picture I got of the company's attitude toward its customers. Under the whimsy you can often sense anxiety; the joke is there, but the humor isn't, the head is catchy but the copy is tense. On the other hand, the tone may be relaxed and the humor consistent; the advertiser may trust his customers to get the point. That's usually a good omen. The same rule of thumb works pretty well for "dignified" ads. If they were pompous and empty I watched my step; if they were merely quietly confident I felt pretty optimistic.

I couldn't find any ads for the statistical firm and I let it go. I still didn't know why they had called me. The manufacturer seemed to be a heavy user of trade publications: there were full pages and double-page spreads in several magazines. I picked out three back issues, counted out forty-five cents for them and slipped them into my briefcase. At first glance, they looked pretty good, but I wanted to take them home and mull them over and see what flavor I could pull out of them.

It wasn't an easy week. I made my rounds, wondering if I should check in with the switchboard girl at Epstein's office at ten-minute intervals and sternly restraining myself from doing it. This was pot-watching. It could only get me churned up about the Gilbrick job and this was a bad state of mind whether I landed it or not. On Monday I went to see the statistical firm and, as I had suspected, the visit was a washout.

You run into this once in awhile. Somebody gets their signals crossed and you're sitting across the desk from a man who thinks he's interviewing an electronics engineer or an income tax accountant. No harm is done in most cases, apart from some embarrassment on their side and some disappointment on yours—unless the firm was like this one.

I stepped through the door and was caught up immediately in what seemed to be an administrative conveyor belt.

"Fill out this card please. Miss Whatzit will see you in just a few minutes."

"But, my appointment was with . . ."

"Fill out this card please. Miss Whatzit sees all Applications preliminarily. Thank you. Take a seat over there, please."

The few minutes became a half-hour. Miss Whatzit, when I finally was admitted to her presence, turned out to have the personality of a recorded announcement.

"Take this questionnaire to the conference room across the hall and complete it please. All questions must be answered fully. Return it to this office when you are finished."

I sat down, uninvited. "Look," I said, "all I have been told is that there is an opening here. I haven't been told what the job is. I may not be qualified for it. We may be able to save my time and yours . . ."

"I cannot discuss personnel procedures with Applicants. Please take the questionnaire to the conference room across the hall . . ."

"Oh, all right."

In the conference room, I glanced through the questionnaire and whistled softly. I'd seen some beauties, but this one looked like a collector's item.

The first page and a half was detailed, but reasonably routine. Name, address, education, previous employment, salaries, description of duties, reasons for leaving and so on. Beyond that point I began to hedge the answers. Where was my bank account and how much? I ignored the first part of the question and simply put down "adequate" for the second. Did I have any sources of income apart from salary? I simply put "yes" without elaborating. Everyone has such sources of income, if you want to count the deposits you get back on bottles. Where was my father born, what was his education, where did he work, how much did he make, what was his position? Where was my mother born, what was her education, was she employed? My wife . . . I skimmed through this section and shook my head. No, not if I sat there a million years, brother.

When I handed the form back to Miss Whatzit, however, she merely swept a cold eye over the pages to make sure they were full and then tossed it into a file basket. She didn't read the answers—I was sure she wouldn't—so she didn't know that many of them simply said "private information." Fifteen minutes later—exactly an hour and a quarter after my arrival—I was ushered into the great man's presence and learned that I was applying for a job as supervisor, data processing department.

"There's no point in wasting your time," I said, "or any more of mine. I have absolutely no qualifications for such a job." I had been simmering slowly for the past hour and now I boiled over. "Oh, by the way," I added. "I want my questionnaire back."

"Your what?"

"The questionnaire I filled out. I want it back. You don't need the information that's on it and you're not entitled to it."

"Oh, *that,*" he said. "No, we need it for our files. It has to go into our files." He pushed a button on his desk and I could hear the buzzer sound in Miss Whatzit's office.

"You obviously do not need it," I replied. "I repeat, you're not entitled to it and what's more"—Miss Whatzit appeared in the door and said something but I ignored her "—what's more, you obtained it under false pretenses."

"Now look here . . ."

"I came up here in perfectly good faith. I had an appointment for three o'clock and I kept it. If *you* had kept it we could have straightened out a perfectly simple mistake in two minutes, but you didn't keep it. You kept me sitting around for an hour and a half while your stooges put me over the jumps. I had to spill my private affairs all over that questionnaire, but *you* couldn't even tell *me* what job I was applying for. And now we find out it isn't one I ever could have applied for and I want the information back. It's none of your business."

"We have a standard procedure for all applicants," he said, "It's just company policy." He nodded to Miss Whatzit and she gave my sleeve a tentative tug.

"I don't work for your company," I snapped, "and I'm not bound by your policy. You seem to think you can go around the world doing just as you damn please and calling it company policy. Well, you can't. Do I get my questionnaire back or do I have to sue you for it?"

With that last, foolish sentence I handed the ball back to him. For a couple of minutes, I think, I had pushed him off balance. He belonged to that breed of petty pryers which feeds on our conditioned compliance. Slap a form down in front of an American and he'll fill it in without asking who wants the information or why. Miss Whatzit's boss counted on that; he didn't know how to handle someone who called his bluff and asked for his credentials. But I had carried it one step too far, I had pulled a bluff of my own and put him back on firm ground.

"You are welcome to sue us if you wish," he said. "And now, if you don't mind . . ."

There was nothing to do but retreat and I did. Miss Whatzit accompanied me all the way to the elevators, probably to forestall any commando raid on her file basket.

By the time I reached the street I was feeling foolish; by the time I was on the train, rolling toward Connecticut, I could see the funny side. I'd made an idiot of myself, that was obvious, and I didn't particularly give a damn. They had probably put me down as a crank and that was okay with me; the word didn't frighten me any more. Look at the richness I had brought into Miss Whatzit's life. She now had a story which would make her the center of attention for the rest of the week. There was nothing like spreading a little joy whenever you could.

In this happy frame of mind, I pulled out my back-issue magazines and had another look at the suburban manufacturer's ads. They were hardly likely to win any awards for originality, and the layouts made me wince. And yet, after dissecting the copy, I decided I liked them. They had an element which was almost indefinable, a certain confidence which suggested the company was genuinely proud of its products. The ads could have been smartened up a little but this air of assurance, this overtone of respect for the customers, is rare and the agency had been wise not to tamper with it. It is also difficult to fake and so it was a reasonably good bet that the advertising actually did reflect the people. If that was the case, they would be more interested in what I had done than who I had been. I'd better take along samples of my work and be ready to talk in professional terms.

Another day had slipped by but it was a reasonably full day and that even included the afternoon's fiasco. Janet was waiting at the station as usual and I launched into the story as soon as I had climbed into the car. "You drive," I said. "I want to tell you about this. I pulled the damnedest scene this afternoon . . ."

|129|

"We had visitors this afternoon," said Janet abruptly.

"Visitors?"

"The police."

"The *police?* "But . . ."

"About Cliff."

"What . . . ?"

"A bunch of kids broke into a garage." Her voice was dry and completely without expression. "They smashed everything in sight. A lot of equipment and things like that."

"Are they claiming Cliff was one of these kids?"

"They know he was. They claim they can prove it."

"Well, now wait a minute," I said. I wasn't putting it together very clearly. "What does Cliff say about it?"

"He hasn't said anything to me. Maybe he'll say something to you."

"Is he . . . did the police actually arrest him or what?"

"I'll begin at the beginning." Janet sounded like someone reading the minutes of the last meeting. "They came around early this afternoon, about one o'clock, I guess. A policeman and a man from the garage. They said they had all the names of the kids who were responsible. They said they had already talked to the kids and they'd all admitted it. I figured they'd gone right to the school first and I didn't like that very much. I told them so but they just sort of shrugged. The position seems to be that they're in our custody —the kids are in their parents' custody, I mean—and we'll all have to appear in court sometime next week."

"What happens then?"

"I'm coming to that. I called Epstein's office right away, but you weren't there. I left a message, but I guess you didn't get it. So I told the other policeman . . ."

"What other policeman?"

"This policeman who called a couple of hours later to see if you were home yet. He said a lot depends on whether the garage presses charges or not. He said they wanted to because this sort of thing was really dangerous and they were determined to put a stop to it. He said they might settle for probation, provided it was really enforced. And the damage, of course; the parents would have to pay for that."

"How much?"

"It hasn't been figured out exactly yet but the policeman kept saying that we were really very lucky. The garage people were willing to talk about it and the damage could have been a lot worse."

"But did he have any idea of *how much?*"

"Just figuring on a preliminary basis," said Janet, "and prorating it among all the parents—that's the way he put it—it will probably be about three hundred dollars apiece."

MAY

"You Blame
Us Kids
for Everything"

Cliff wasn't home when I got there; he had taken advantage of Janet's brief absence to clear out. It was probably a good thing he did because I was mad as hell. If Janet had blown three hundred bucks on a coat, I would have called this the height of irresponsibility. It would have been an understandable act, however; foolish but understandable, and we would at least have had the coat to show for it. But to hurl us three hundred dollars into debt for the dubious pleasure of sheer destruction . . .

The first thing I did was to call the investigating officer who was still at his desk and who repeated his statement that we had been very lucky. "They smashed some windshields and a glass counter and wrecked an engine analyzer," he told me. "It could have been a lot worse." He seemed cheerful enough about the whole business. Possibly, it was just routine to him. I said thanks and hung up and Janet began phoning around the neighborhood in an effort to locate Cliff. I was having the wrong reactions, I could see that. I was like the parents in the television programs; the ones who are responsible if their children run off the rails. Sometimes they give the kids too little attention and sometimes they give them too much attention and sometimes they give them the wrong sort of attention, but it is always the fault of the parents. And here I was, worrying about three hundred dollars.

It wasn't the cash, it was what it meant and what Cliff knew it meant. He could see his mother working to bring in a little extra cash and his father scraping to save a nickel here and a dime there; he knew the family was in a hole and he knew as clearly as a fourteen-year-old possibly could know that every dollar gained or lost could shape his own future and his little brother's life. A couple of generations ago he would have been sent out to work in the mines or the factories; now all he had been asked to do was to make his contribution by exercising a little restraint. He had been asked to help and this was his answer.

"I can't think of anyone else to call," said Janet.

"Let it go," I told her. "He'll show up."

"What are you going to say to him?"

"I don't know," I said. "I haven't figured this out yet. I don't even know how I feel about it."

It wasn't much of an evening. We talked about Cliff, but the talk kept going around in circles and it was obvious that the theories we had learned didn't fit the reality we faced. I thought back to my own childhood and the busted windows and the damaged shrubbery. What had my parents done? The answer was—nothing. The age of permissiveness had already begun and they had been terrorized by the fear that they might raise their children unscientifically.

Cliff came home about midnight and we sent him to bed without comment. He was up early the next morning—apparently he intended to slip out of the house quietly—but I was expecting this and I intercepted him at the door.

"You'd better come into the kitchen and have some breakfast," I said.

"But I'll be late to school."

"What were you going to do, walk there?"

"Well, I . . ."

"You'll find the hitchhiking a bit tough at this hour," I said. "Come and have some breakfast. I want you to stick around anyway."

I took some coffee into the living room and waited. Janet was in the kitchen, feeding Cliff and keeping an eye on him and she brought him in when he had finished.

"Sit down," I said.

"I don't want to."

"Frankly, I don't give a damn whether you sit or stand so you may as well sit. You'll be more comfortable."

He sat down on the edge of the sofa and glared at the wall.

"Let's get this sorted out," I began. "Were you with this gang and did you smash up this garage?"

"I didn't do anything much."

"Then you weren't with them?"

"Well, maybe I was *with* them, but . . ."

"You'd better make up your mind," I told him. "This isn't a question of who busted the spring on the screen door. You're in trouble with the law, get that through your head, and if you tell me you weren't there, then that's what we'll go into court with. So let's just forget this 'maybe' stuff. Were you in that garage? Yes or no?"

"Well, okay, so I went along with them."

"The police say some windshields and some of the garage equipment were smashed. That right?"

He shifted his position and looked at Janet and then at me and then at the wall again.

"Come on," I said. "Was the stuff smashed or wasn't it?"

"Well . . . maybe a windshield got busted."

"One windshield?"

"Look," he said. "You keep talking like I did everything. It wasn't my idea, I just went along."

"I didn't ask whose idea it was. I'm trying to find out how much you had to do with it. I gather you just went along. Did you just happen to do some of the smashing, too?"

He looked around the room again. "Well," he whispered. "Maybe a little."

"How much is a little? One windshield? Two? The shop counter? I understand that was broken up, too."

"The other guys did most of it," he said. "The way you keep talking, it was all my fault. Why don't you blame some of the other guys?"

"Because you're just as much to blame as they are. That's what the law says, you know. This business of 'I just went along' and 'I just did a little bit' won't wash in court. You'd better get that straight; the guy that thinks up the idea and the guy who goes along with it are both responsible; *you're* equally responsible with the others."

This roused him in some obscure way to indignation.

"Sure, you blame us kids. You're always blaming us for everything. We didn't ask to be born . . ."

"What the hell do you think the rest of us did," I interrupted, "file applications?"

"And . . and . . we're living in a world we never made and . . ."

"Now just one minute," I snapped. "There's one thing you're not going to do and that's sit there and answer questions by parroting a lot of half-baked slogans. You're fourteen years old and you can read and write and you're old enough to start making up your own excuses. If you're going to hate somebody or smash something, at least have guts enough to do it on your own hook. Don't start serving up a lot of second-hand justifications, because I won't take them."

"I . . ."

"Besides," I added, "there's one complaint you won't have any more. From now on, you *are* going to be living in a world you made. And so am I and so is your mother and so is your brother and we'll all be stuck with it whether we like it or not. So just think that over while you're thinking about who's responsible for what. Now get your books together; you have to get to school and I have to get to the station."

When we got to the station, after we'd dropped the kids off at school, I swung the car around beside the platform and sat for a moment with my hands resting on the steering wheel.

"You know," I said, "my father used to tell a story. One time when he was—oh, I don't know, sixteen or seventeen, maybe—he and a bunch of other kids got their hands on a couple of buckets of paint and threw it all over the front steps of their school. The steps and the sidewalk. Next day they were all lined up in the principal's office—five or six of them. The principal said he guessed it was just high spirits and since no real harm was done, he wasn't going to punish them. They all brightened up at that, of course.

|135|

Then he said, something like this: 'Of course, it's your project and it's only half done. You put the paint on, so now you can take it off. But I don't want you to think I'm punishing you. Any time you think you'd rather do this than anything else you might be doing, that's your business. You go right ahead and do it. You've got a right to throw all the paint that you're willing to scrub off.' So then he marched them down to the basement to get brushes and turpentine from the janitor and they spent the next two weekends getting paint out of cement, inch by inch."

A car pulled up behind me and the driver honked once, briefly.

"My father used to say," I added, "that the thing he learned was how easy it was to throw paint on something and how hard it was to take it off. He worked it out later on; it had cost him two hours of scrubbing for every one minute of throwing."

"Suppose he'd smashed something beyond repair?" asked Janet. "How would the wise old principal have handled that?"

The guy behind me began leaning on his horn.

"I don't know," I said. "I don't know how you'd scrub away destruction."

I got out of the car and Janet slid over behind the wheel.

"Try not to worry about it," she said. "It will work out somehow."

I did worry about it, of course. I was feeling surrounded, sniped at front and rear. The world may present problems, but trouble in your own home breeds a special kind of helplessness. You can fight the things that come at you from the front. If one route is blocked you can try another; if one day goes wrong, there's always tomorrow. But there's only one door to your own home and it has to be the right door; you can't go down the road and open another. Everything you've got goes into prying out one extra dollar, one extra hour, one extra bit of recognition—and somebody at home is casually canceling it all out. While I was scrubbing my own paint off the steps, Cliff was throwing more.

There were three ads in the mail at the office, nothing more. I flipped open my attaché case, dumped the contents on the desk and looked at them with distaste. There was plenty of paperwork to do: a list of a half-dozen letters to write, the résumé to check

over and update for my call on the manufacturer, some homework
on the Gilbrick organization, just in case. Gilbrick! If they did intend to call, I hoped to God they'd put it off for one more day.
I didn't feel up to fencing with Gilbrick himself or Lewis or Heath
or . . .

The telephone rang.

It had to happen, of course. Fate, that lousiest of stage direc-
tors, couldn't let a chance like this slip by. I took a deep breath
and picked up the receiver.

"God dammit," said a rasping voice, "why can't you let a guy
know where you're hiding?"

"Phil! Is that you?"

"You're damn right it's me. The question is, is that *you?* I've
called your house five, six, times . . . ."

"Janet's working now."

"Oh. Well, how about some lunch?"

"You bet. There's an Automat . . ."

"Oh, come on over to Philippe's," said Phil. "I'll put you on
my expense account."

I was pretty sure he couldn't do it, but I was too weak-willed to
argue. A martini at noon! Coq au vin instead of cheese
sandwiches!

"Okay," I answered, "make it Philippe's."

The place hadn't changed much. It was still noisy and crowded
and Philippe himself still presided at the door, making his face to
shine upon an occasional customer but withholding the warmth of
his smile from the huddled masses yearning to be fed. It should
have been something of a thrill, walking in there again, but it wasn't.
The place looked boring.

Phil arrived a few minutes late and full of apologies. He was
clutching the familiar briefcase and wearing the familiar grin, but
his eyes looked tired and there were lines of strain around his
mouth. Over our plates, we traded the experiences of the past few
weeks. Phil's had been routine; at least that was what he claimed.
As he talked about them, however, something began to come out,
a certain restlessness touched with bitterness. He was spending
more time in the office and less on the road; a hundred small responsibilities had replaced a few big ones.

"It's sort of a perpetual paper chase," he said. "Memo here, report there, meetings, projects. Stick stuff in the files on Monday, pull it out on Tuesday. You come up with an idea, nobody says no, nobody says yes. Very interesting, they say. We must look into this . . . Then they kiss it to death. Sometimes it seems to me like there isn't any Tuesday or Wednesday in the week. I just come in and work the same Monday over and over again."

"I suppose," I said, "that one answer might be switching jobs. But I'm not going to be the guy to say it. Not me."

"Let it go; I'm lucky to be on a payroll. It's just that all the fun's gone out of the job, but I guess that must sound like a pretty thin complaint to you. Is there *anything* in sight?"

I told him about Gilbrick and the suburban manufacturer. He knew nothing about Gilbrick though he had heard of them, but he did know something about the manufacturing firm and had a fairly high opinion of it. I also told him about the statistical firm.

"Well," he said, "it looks like you've met him."

"Met who?"

"The guy who kicks the cat when nobody's looking. I told you you would. You don't seem any the worse for it. Better, maybe." He fiddled with his martini glass for a moment, turning the stem between his fingers. "There's one thing I wanted to ask you," he said finally, "but it isn't really any of my business. I mean, if you don't want to answer, that's okay and no bones broken. Just say so."

"What's that?"

"How are your finances?"

"Phil," I answered, "I quit being sensitive about money last year and you can ask anything you want. Theoretically we ran out of money six months ago; actually we've managed to bump along from week to week though I'm damned if I know how. Janet's got a job—I told you about that—and we sold one of the cars and as for the rest of it; well, there's just a hell of a lot of things you figure into a budget because you can't get along without them. Then the time comes when you have to and so—you do. This is . . ."

"What?"

"Uh, nothing. As I said, we're scraping along." I was going to say "This the first drink I've had since Christmas" purely as an illustration, but it might have embarrassed Phil.

"You Blame Us Kids
for Everything"

He seemed embarrassed anyway. The martini glass revolved two or three more times in his hand and he cleared his throat.

"Well . . ." he said, "the thing is, that I was going to suggest—if you should be . . . uh . . . short, that maybe I could loan you a little bit. Now look," he added, "I don't know why this sort of thing always has to be so damn awkward. It takes money to get things done, that's all. I've got a little and you're welcome to have the use of it. When you don't need it any more, you can give it back. Why don't you let me write you a check for . . . for five hundred, say. If you're getting by as it is, fine. You just stick it in the bank. Some opportunity comes up, you'll be able to grab it. Some emergency comes up—one of the kids gets sick, maybe—you're covered. This way you'll have something behind you and when you've got something behind you it shows. Believe me, it shows. Now, how about it?"

I had seen where the conversation was heading and I had been working out a gracious refusal, but that word "kids" started a new train of thought. I was going to get a bill and I was going to have to go to somebody with my pride in my hand and borrow the money to pay it. Up to that moment, there had been only one person to approach and that was Melly. Melly would say yes, there was no doubt about that. You had to hand Melly one thing; he might be slow to pick up a bar bill but he was a fast man with a dollar if any member of the clan needed help. He'd hand it over promptly, with a little lecture on parental responsibilities.

"Dammit," said Phil, "I knew I'd put my foot in my mouth."

"No, no, you haven't. I was just thinking, that's all. The truth is, Phil . . ."

I told him the whole story. ". . . so the fact is," I finished, "that I'm going to get hit with this business. I don't know yet how much it will be. They think around three hundred or so and there may be other costs . . ." I was thinking of the possibility that we might need a lawyer, though I hoped we wouldn't. ". . . so I just might take you up on that offer *if* . . ."

"Well, sure . . ."

"*If*," I repeated firmly, "you really can spare it, Phil. What I'm wondering now is whether *I'm* embarrassing *you*. Do you *really* have that dough, Phil?"

"Sure I do."

[139]

"To spare?"

"I've got it to spare. I was going to buy a canoe and paddle around the world, but that can wait until next year. Now let's get this over with before we both pass out from self-consciousness."

He wrote out the check and handed it across the table to me.

"One other thing," he added. "If the bill comes to four-ninety, don't come rushing around to return the odd ten. Buy yourself a bottle of Scotch with it, for God's sake."

I got back to the office, slightly dizzy from the unaccustomed drinking and more than slightly late, to be told by the switchboard operator that Janet had been trying to reach me. I called her immediately and fidgeted while the operator made the connections. A long-distance call in our household was like a telegram in the old days; it almost had to be bad news. We didn't make them otherwise. I was praying that kid hadn't . . .

"Hello?" said Janet's voice in my ear.

"It's me. What's wrong?"

"Oh, it's next week, next Tuesday."

"What is?"

Janet sounded slightly indignant.

"The hearing, of course. I thought I'd better phone instead of waiting until you got home in case you were making any appointments. We have to be there."

"I *want* to be there."

"Well, we have to. And another thing. I've had three calls today from the other parents. I mean parents of some of the other kids."

"What about?"

"Mainly to find out what we're doing or what we're going to do." She mentioned the names, but I didn't know any of them. "One of them was sort of nasty, I thought. She didn't say it in so many words, but she kept hinting that her kid was led into it by Cliff and the others and that we should admit it. Then there was this man, one of the fathers. He kept trying to find out where he could reach you and talking about lining up some good lawyers and so on . . ."

"Did he think his little darling was a victim, too?"

"Well, he seemed to think they all were. He was saying things about it's happening every day and it wasn't so bad and what the hell, the garage was going to get paid and things like that. He said

the garage was probably padding its bill for the damage and would
come out of it pretty damn well—that's the way he put it."

"What did you tell them?"

"Nothing much. I just said we were still thinking about it and I
got them off the line as quickly as I could. I think the woman was
mad."

"Well, let her be," I said. It sounded as if some of these people
were panicking and I had no desire to get mixed up with schemes
or theories which might just make the situation worse. "You go
right on handling it the same way. If anyone calls up and talks
sensibly . . . well, maybe we'll call them back."

"Okay," said Janet, and she hung up before I had a chance to
mention Phil and the check.

I gave myself the rest of the afternoon off. This is poor policy
for the job hunter as a rule; few things are more emotionally ex-
hausting than killing time and each day killed is a small suicide.
You hang around, wishing the hours past and hating yourself because the most precious commodity in the world has become a
burden. Someplace in the country somebody has started a book or
finished a painting or signed a contract or given birth to a baby or
moved a scientific search one step closer to discovery, and all in
those hours you passed through so painfully.

I just felt I needed some air. The material for the manufacturer
was packed neatly in my attaché case, ready for the meeting the
next day, and nothing else was urgent. Strictly speaking, I should
have hung around in case the Gilbrick people called, but I no
longer wasted time on the dragged-out cases. If it hadn't been for
Epstein's optimism, I'd have crossed them off the list the previous
week.

I strolled down Fifth Avenue for a few blocks and then, on a
sudden impulse, I ducked into a subway station, hopped a train for
the Battery and boarded a Staten Island ferry. It was a mild day in
mid-Manhattan, a slightly close day with a hint in the air of the
soggy summer heat to come. Out on the bay, however, the wind
was brisk and the air was clean and sharp and even chilly. An
ocean liner, one of the big Cunarders, was slipping down the river
toward the Narrows, outward bound for Cherbourg and Southamp-
ton. The ferry altered course to pass under her stern and I could
see the passengers, high up on the black steel wall, peering down at

me. For some foolish reason I waved and some of them waved back, returning the traveler's traditional salute.

Behind me, the city shrank to a travel poster, a cluster of towers and spires so clean-cut and imposing that it was difficult to believe it could ever hold any fear or ugliness. On the return trip, I knew, it would grow again, becoming separate buildings and then streets and then crowds and finally, when I stepped into the poster, one tiny, windowless cubicle. Meanwhile, it was bright on the bay and the wind was blowing away some of my staleness.

The trip took longer than I thought and I made it back to Grand Central, breathless but enormously refreshed, with only a few minutes to spare. On the train I relaxed in my seat and tried to analyze the situation at home. Some of it, obviously, was out of our hands; the law would grind out its decision and there was very little we could do but cross our fingers and hope. The facts were clear-cut and, apart from entering a plea in extenuation, there seemed to be very little we could do. Where did we go from here? How could we discipline the boy? Mere lecturing wouldn't help, I could see that. Slapping a curfew on him might, but how would we go about enforcing it? The law itself was no deterrent; I was already aware that probation was regarded as a joke and as something of a distinction among the kids. However I viewed the matter, I kept coming back to the same paradox: a teen-ager was regarded legally as a child and socially as an adult. Just how did you deal with an adult who couldn't be held to account for the things he did?

"Get a good grip on yourself," said Janet, when she met me at the station. "Melly and Marge are coming over this evening."

I asked her why she let them come. It took me about five minutes to ask it.

"They insisted," said Janet. "They want to help. Short of setting fire to the house, I can't think of any way to stop them."

"Okay," I said. "Let's go home and set fire to the house."

I told her about Phil's loan. That question, at least, wouldn't have to come up. I braced myself for the rest of it, but when they arrived after supper, Melly was oddly subdued. Perhaps Marge had given him a talking to before they came over, perhaps his perception was a bit sharper when it came to actual emergencies. He only got out of line, in the old Melly mannner, once during the evening.

"You Blame Us Kids
for Everything"

"I just can't imagine something like this happening in Our Family," he complained. "There's a lot of it going on, I know that. You read about it in the newspapers. But having it right . . . ah . . right here . . ."

It was the illusion of immunity; I recognized it because my first reaction had been pretty much the same. We used to feel this way during the war. You knew that so many guys were going to get it in the next few days, but it was going to be somebody else. Not you, never you. You were okay until it occurred to you one day that the guys who had been hit probably had felt the same way. After that, you got scared sometimes. Now I was thinking there were probably hundreds, perhaps thousands of families who just couldn't imagine something like this happening, right up to the moment they answered the doorbell and found a cop standing on the doorstep.

". . . don't you think so?"

I realized Melly was still talking.

"Oh, sure," I said, "absolutely. Sure."

"Well, I'm glad you agree because I've always felt, fundamentally, I mean, that . . ."

He went on and on and I just sat there, tuning him out. Whatever he was saying he was probably right, or he would be if the world were the logical place Melly imagined it to be. Certain things just don't happen; that was Melly's view. But they did and you either knew that or you didn't.

". . . nice boy, always been a nice boy. Can't imagine what got into . . ."

Sorry, Melly, but he isn't a particularly nice boy. Kids are never very nice; their judgments are largely instinctive and their instincts are largely animal. Sometimes we manage to create that particular form of inhibition known as civilization; sometimes, but not always.

Still, Melly was there to help; I had to remember that. He might not be what you'd call a good old buddy, but most of the good old buddies had taken to their heels a long time ago and there was one thing Melly didn't do, he didn't run away. I realized that and I appreciated it, but I was just too tired that evening to cope with any conversation. I was going to get up the next day and call on the suburban manufacturer and I just didn't feel up to it. I didn't want to answer any more questions or put on any more little acts; I wanted to go someplace where they knew me and where nothing had to be explained to anyone.

The next day's appointment served as an excuse for easing Melly and Marge out the door at an early hour. I went back to the living room and took my shoes off and, at that point, the phone rang. Janet picked up the receiver.

"Hello? Yes, it is. No, he isn't. Well, I'm sorry, but he missed his usual train and I don't expect him home until quite. . . . Well, I'd rather not, if you don't mind; I imagine he'll be very tired when he gets home and . . . Of *course* we're taking it seriously; I can assure you we're every bit as concerned about it as you are, we just haven't had a chance. . . . Yes, I'll tell him. Goodbye. Yes, I'll be sure to mention that. Good . . . yes, I'll remember. Goodbye."

She hung up the phone and shrugged.

"The same man," she explained. "The one that called this afternoon."

"Same answer. Let's skip it."

"I'm supposed to remind you that there's only a week left."

"Thanks," I said. "I wasn't in much danger of forgetting. What's he want to do, appeal it to the Supreme Court?"

"Something like that, I guess."

"Well, I don't know." I sat for a moment, staring at my shoes. "Maybe we should be doing something. It just seems to me that this is a very good time for people to keep their mouths shut. I don't see how we can improve the situation and somebody could just start fooling around and make it worse."

I'd meant to turn in early but I didn't. Melly and Marge had knocked my evening out of gear and I felt peculiar—too tired to stay up and too restless to go to bed. I flicked on the TV set and tried several channels—one Western, one drama of misunderstood youth which I cut off right in the middle of ". . . world I never . . ."; one Italian film with subtitles, one 1934-style musical movie. I settled for the musical and I found its magnificent silliness as effective as it had been thirty years ago, when it had been made for other tired and discouraged people. The soundtrack was thin and tinny and the murky picture blurred and jiggled until my eyes began to smart and I closed them. It was past midnight when Janet woke me up so I could go to bed.

Cliff had put on a new personality the next morning, a tough-guy pose apparently drawn from some teen-ager's hero. I bore it through breakfast, but when he shoved his brother aside and came swaggering out to the car I told him to take his thumbs out of his belt, go back to the front door and come out properly. This got the day off to a bad start for all of us and I decided, after we'd dropped the kids off at school, that I had been mistaken.

"Maybe," said Janet. "I think you have to remember that he could be pretty scared."

"I hope so. No, I don't mean that; I don't want him scared or repentent either. If there was just one way of getting across some . . . some sense of proportion."

I turned into the station yard and pulled up beside the platform.

"Oh, well," I added. "We've got a week to do it in."

I squirmed around to get my attaché case out of the rear seat. When I had it in my lap I clicked it open one last time just to make sure it was all in there, my résumés and my notes and the name and address of the man I was going to see.

"This is the sort of trip that gets on my nerves," I said. "Into the city on one railroad, out again on another. It wastes so much time and I hate those damn trains."

"Why don't you take the car?" Janet said. "I can take the bus over to Max's place."

"How would you and the kids get home?"

"We could get a lift. I'll call around and find somebody who can pick me up at work before they call for their own kids."

It was a temptation and I thought it over for a moment, but Janet was making the whole business of lining up a lift sound easy. Maybe it would be, if she was lucky; on the other hand, maybe it wouldn't. I could get where I was going by train and there was supposed to be a bus which ran right from the station to the plant. It was one of the days when we both needed the car but she obviously needed it more, with both herself and the kids to worry about.

"Thanks," I said, "but let it go. I've done this before, remember? It's just these change-here-and-change-there junkets—they get on my nerves."

|145|

The Job Hunter: The Diary
of a "Lost" Year

The drag into New York was as dull as usual and there was nobody interesting on the train. I stopped at the office on my way between stations and riffled quickly through the mail, but there was nothing of any importance there, either. Half an hour later I was in a train seat again, rolling through another set of suburbs and trying to gauge from glimpses how they looked and what they would be like to live in.

The factory wasn't easy to find. "Number six bus," said the man behind the little wicket in the suburban station. "Ride it out to Ocean Avenue and then walk down the road a hundred—hundred-fifty yards maybe—and you'll see it. Big brick building with one of them glassy fronts." I waited outside the bus stop beside the station for twenty minutes or so, scanning each bus which drove up, before I found out that the number six, for some reason, left from the other side of the street. Another ten minutes went by before one came along.

"How much is the fare?" I asked.

"Huh?"

"The fare, how much?"

"Oh, the *fare*," he said. "Fifteen."

I dropped a nickel and a dime in the box and asked him to let me know when we got to Ocean Avenue.

"Ocean Avenue?"

"Yes."

"Or Ocean Street?"

"Uh . . . Ocean Avenue, I guess."

"*Oh* . . . kay." His tone implied that he wasn't responsible for people who went to Ocean Avenue and when we got there I saw why. It was a bare intersection, marked only by a highway sign and a mailbox, surrounded by brown, marshy meadows.

"Ocean *Avenue*," the driver said, and, since there was nothing else to do, I stepped off the bus and watched it roll away. There were a few scattered shacks on one side of the road, a lumberyard a couple of hundred yards or so down the other side but no place was there anything that resembled a big brick building with one of them glassy fronts. I was lost and I began cursing. I was not cursing the man who had misdirected me or myself for being too slow-witted to ask the bus driver if he knew the company, but the fate which had deprived me of the second car. Behind the wheel I would have made a U-turn and doubled back until I found a gas station. On foot I could merely stand at that bleak crossroads, feeling like a turtle without its shell.

I stood for five minutes or so, helplessly watching the cars whip by. Then a pickup truck slid out of the stream of traffic and slowed for a turn. On impulse I stepped into the road, flagged it down and asked directions.

"You're practically there," said the driver. "It's just down the road."

"How far?"

"Oh . . . couple miles." That was the station man's hundred yards or so. "Give you a lift down, if you want. I'm going right by."

I thanked him fervently and climbed into the truck. At least I'd make it to the plant; how I'd get back again was another question, but I'd worry about that after the interview.

"Had a breakdown?" asked the truck driver.

"No, I was coming out by bus."

"Which bus?"

"Number six."

"Number *six?* Been me, I'da taken the Oak Street bus. Goes long way round, of course."

"Does it go closer to the plant, though?"

"Goes *to* the plant. Six is quicker though, providing you don't mind walking a couple of miles."

"I think," I said, "I'll try the Oak Street bus going back."

He dropped me off at the front gate of the factory and I glanced at my watch. It could have been worse; I had allowed myself plenty of time and I was only fifteen minutes late.

The man I had come to see—he held the starkly utilitarian title of "division manager"—waved my apologies aside. "Happens all the time," he said. "Hard place to find. Excuse me a minute." He began flipping through a stack of papers, shoving some to one side, initialing others with a fast flick of his ballpoint pen and shooting them into a basket. He was a small man, compact and wiry, with thinning gray hair and a brown, seamed face which hinted at long exposure to wind and sun at some period in his life. His

|147|

office, like his title, was plain. Behind the desk, steel-framed windows looked out over a gravel parking lot; in the opposite wall, a big rectangle—fibreboard, possibly, or some sort of insulating material—had been set in where a second set of windows or an extension of the office had been boarded up. Scattered around the walls haphazardly were a couple of group photographs, rust-colored with age; three cartoons cut from magazines and cheaply framed, and two remarkably fine ship prints. A heavy table was littered with sales material and various electrical components and a brass valve served as a paperweight. Filling the office, but apparently coming from some outside point, was a deep sound, felt rather than heard; a muffled thumping like a giant's heartbeat.

"Now then!"

He picked up the last piece of paper in the stack and I recognized my résumé. He muttered through it in an undertone, peering at me occasionally as if he were trying to match the paragraphs with the man sitting on the other side of his desk.

"Well," he said finally, "I thought I'd seen your name someplace before. That advertising award, that's what it was. Good campaign. I remember it."

It was a lie, of course; a wonderful lie which lifted me like a shot of good brandy. Having boosted my morale, however, he proceeded to test it. "This is sort of a comedown for you, isn't it?" he asked.

"Well, I . . . no, of course not."

"Oh, come on, now. Plush office, fancy title, and now you're making the rounds of factories in the sticks . . ."

The phone rang and he picked it up.

"Yeah? Why? What was wrong with that last shipment? Umph. Umph. Yup. Well, tell him if he's got any beefs to get on the phone and tell me about them. I can't do anything if he just keeps howling like a dog that's sitting on a nail and is too lazy to get up . . ."

He hung up.

"Have you seen any of our ads?" he asked.

"Yes, several of them."

"Which ones?"

I mentioned a couple of them and he pushed back his chair, walked over to the cluttered table and picked up a magazine.

"How about this one?"

"You Blame Us Kids
for Everything"

It was what I would call an average trade book ad, a little brighter and breezier than most, topped by a head which began: "Where Quality Is Routine." He obviously expected some comment so I said politely that it was very good.

"No," he answered, "I don't think it is, particularly; not by the standards you're used to. It could be better." He sat on the edge of the table and began swinging one leg. "The point is, you see, that. . . . oh, hell."

The phone was ringing again.

"Yeah? They took *both* prints of the film? Well, you better get another from. . . . Oh, it's this afternoon. No, no, you wouldn't have time. No, *don't* put the appointment off, don't ever do that. You've seen the film, haven't you? You know what it says? Okay, Harry, you just get over there and say the same thing. Put the samples in front of him and talk specs and if he has a question, make sure you have an answer for it. If he wants 'Gone With The Wind,' we won't sell him anyway."

"As I was saying," he continued, hanging up the phone again and strolling back to the table, "we do our selling under certain restrictions. We do some puffing, of course; we do all we can, but the head on that ad is literally true. Quality *is* routine here. We have our customers sitting right in our laps. The stuff we turn out is handled by skilled workmen and checked by professional inspectors. We never have any doubts about what they're thinking; they call up and tell us."

He gestured toward the big rectangle on the wall.

"Some of the machinery's right on the other side of that wall. My predecessor had windows there so he could watch it. I had them covered over because the machines were just too damn loud, but I can still hear them running. Know what would happen if they stopped?"

"I guess you'd be in a jam."

"Well, that's the least of it. Companies all across the country would be in a jam. They have schedules which depend on our stuff arriving on time. I'm sorry to spell out the obvious like this but— we've taken on some drop-outs from the affluent society. It's always a shock to them to find out that the work here is just as tough and the standards are just as high."

The intercom on his desk buzzed and he leaned over and

flipped the switch. In the anguished squawking I caught only the word "deliveries."

"Why, no, it isn't our usual practice."

Rawk wheeple wong wong blaat!

"Oh, all right, if he thinks it will work, tell him to go ahead and we'll hold the prayer meeting later. Just remind him," my host added with appalling cheerfulness, "that it's my neck if he's wrong."

He sat down behind his desk and picked up my résumé again.

"We don't go in for committees very much here," he said. "Or meetings or memos. We need people who can take over a job and run it and make their decisions and be responsible for them. Sometimes . . ." he nodded wryly at the intercom ". . . this means getting out on a limb a little. Maybe I ought to warn you that this is not only tough but it can be catching. Men get to like it. So . . . while we're thinking you over, maybe you can be thinking us over, too. Now there's a few points . . ."

For the next few minutes he fired questions at me, shrewd, specific questions aimed at what he probably would have called "the specs." What, exactly, did this job involve? What, precisely, did that title mean? The quiz was brief, but by the time it ended I had spilled more information about the work I had actually done than in any previous interview.

"Okay," he said, "thanks. I hope I'll be seeing you again. If I don't—good luck."

On the Oak Street bus, going "the long way around," I tried to sort out my impressions. "Think us over," he had said and I thought him over. Tough? Yes, so tough he could open the interview by giving away a big slice of something wonderful. It wasn't the award; there are hundreds of awards and I had merely tossed a mention of mine into the résumé for what it was worth. He could have given me the same lift with some other lie—"I've seen your work," perhaps, or "I've heard of you." At any rate, he didn't need an upper hand and he liked to deal with equals, that was obvious. And so he had found a few words which lifted me above the mob of anonymous men who trudge around with their hats in their hands, a few words which put me back on a professional plane. It was ironic, I thought, how many firms spend millions reaching for something like this and never quite grasp it,

|150|

and here was this guy in his Spartan office with the fibreboard wall who had put his finger on it. If you can give a man self-respect with one simple sentence and that sentence is more than you can afford, then your money will never be quite enough. There are companies which give millions to charity, but these few words are beyond their resources and the people who work for them are always poor, though one benefit is heaped upon another. What a strange world it is, where we fight to give people equality and then deny them humanity.

As for the company itself, there really wasn't much to think over; a job was a job and if they offered me one I'd take it. The odds here were the same as the odds on any other interview; one of the first things you have to learn, if you're going to stay right side up, is that it doesn't pay to judge your chances by the cordiality of your reception. This was a nice guy and I was grateful for the psychological boost, but he was also a practical guy and he'd hire the man he believed to be the best bet. In the same practical way I would put him on my list and make my follow-up phone calls and downgrade the lead as the days dragged by and fresh possibilities popped up.

The rest of the week was routine. I spent most of it in the office, culling Epstein's trade magazines for personnel ads and trying to cook up new opening paragraphs for the covering letters I sent with résumés. The weekend was taut and unpleasant. The father who had been harassing Janet on the phone showed up in person. He was calling on everyone, he said, to "make sure we all stuck together when we went in there next Tuesday so they didn't put anything over on us." He was an impressive-looking man with square shoulders and a firm jaw, and he obviously was scared stiff. You could see him rallying the boys in the boardroom to tackle a competitor and that, apparently, was what he was trying to do now. He couldn't do it, of course; he couldn't do anything. He was as helpless as the rest of us. It was a bit early in the year to sit on the patio but I took him around there anyway and did my best to calm him down. This just made him angry and he went away complaining that he couldn't, for God's sake, get anyone to *do* anything.

Cliff spent most of the day wandering around the neighborhood and this didn't make me very happy, either. On Sunday, I restricted him to the house and the yard. "Not that anyone with an ounce of judgment would get into another jam at this exact moment," I said, "but if you had an ounce of judgment you wouldn't be in this one. I think we'll just play it safe."

I played with the idea of staying home Monday and saving the fare, but I finally decided to go in. There was the division manager, he might call, and there just might be some replies to a couple of letters I sent out the previous week. One actually did come in, but it didn't require any action. It said no.

I didn't feel very well Tuesday morning; I guess none of us did. Janet phoned Max to remind him that she'd be coming in late and I ate some eggs that tasted like cardboard and then drove young Skip to school. When I got back to the house I inspected Cliff to make sure he was presentable and then led him into the living room and told him to sit down on the sofa.

"I don't know how they run these things," I told him, "so I don't know what you may be asked. Whatever it is, however, you'll be smart if you tell the truth. Now try to get it through your head that I'm not delivering a moral lecture; I'm giving you the best advice I can. I don't know what you've built up in your own mind about this, but if you have any idea you're some sort of martyr— or some sort of hero, for that matter—forget it. These people have seen a thousand snotty kids and they know all the answers. If you start putting on an act of some sort they'll tie you up in knots. So if they start asking, just tell it the way it happened. That's all."

I glanced at my watch and waited for a couple of minutes, but he didn't have any reply.

"Okay," I said, "let's go."

I don't know what I expected; something off the order of a courtroom drama on television, perhaps. The hearing was "informal" however, and after a week of tension, it was almost an anticlimax. The garage owner and the arresting officers told their stories and the boys were asked, one by one, if they had anything to say. Cliff and his five playmates, three looking solemn and two grinning broadly, shook their heads in turn. The judge, a middle-aged man with a somewhat harassed expression, polled the parents to make sure they were all in the courtroom and then riffled through some papers on his desk.

"Ahh . . . it's my understanding that no charges are being

pressed in this case . . . ah . . . subject to payment for the damage,
of course. That amounts to . . . ah . . . here we are . . . three hundred and seventy-eight dollars and sixty-seven cents for each . . .
ah . . . lad involved. Now . . . ah . . . this is a first offense in each
case so the court's judgment will be the same for all five—
probation for a period of one year."

He stared sternly at the five boys.

"Do you lads understand what that means?"

One said "Yessir" in a thin voice; the other four—including
Cliff—remained silent.

"Good . . . good. I don't want to see you in here again."

I remained in my seat for a moment or so before I realized the
hearing was over. In the corridor outside, the man who had come
to my house Saturday was talking earnestly to another father while
a small, fierce little woman was insisting that the other boys had
led her Henry astray.

The garage owner came by and I stopped him, on impulse, and
told him I was sorry the whole foolish business had happened.

"Oh, hell," he said. "Kids . . ." He shrugged.

"Not my kids," I told him. "Not from now on."

The garage man stared at Cliff keenly for a moment. "One
thing I'm curious about," he said, finally. "What was the point,
son? What have you kids got against me?"

A red flush spread over Cliff's face. He made a small noise
which might have been a reply, but I didn't catch it.

"Go on," I said, "tell him. He's entitled to know."

"We didn't do nuthin'," the boy mumbled. "We were just havin'
some fun."

"Then you really didn't have anything against me; you just
thought it would be fun to smash something?"

"But . . ." Cliff looked wildly at me and then at the garage man
again. "But . . . we didn't know it was *you*."

"It was someone," I told him. "It's always someone. Remember
that."

I kept my mouth shut on the way home and let it sink in. The
meeting had been accidental and somewhat melodramatic but most
children and a good many adults can't learn any other way. One
other thought did strike me as we turned into the driveway and I
rammed that home, too.

"Since you were just having fun," I said, "I hope you got four hundred dollars worth of fun out of it—more fun than anything else that money would have bought. A boat, for example."

I put the car away and shut the garage doors and went into the house.

"I gather you're not going into the city," Janet said.

"Hell, no."

"How about some lunch, then? It's past noon."

"Oh . . . all right. A sandwich, maybe. Just let me give the office a ring and make sure nothing's come up." Janet's eyebrows rose. "It costs less than the train fare would have if I'd gone in today," I reminded her.

I sat down on the end of the sofa beside the telephone table and took off my shoes. Then I picked up the phone and called Epstein's switchboard girl.

"Hi," she said, cheerfully. "You didn't miss much. Couple letters and one phone call. He said call him back when you got a chance."

"Who was it?"

"Hang on a minute, I got it here someplace. Here it is—a Mr. Lewis from Gil . . . looks like Gilbrick."

"He's Always Chasing Something He Can't Catch Up With"

For all their personal peculiarities, the Gilbrick people were solid businessmen. A good product at a fair price; that was the way they had built their company and you could trust the Gilbrick label. They knew you had to spend money to make money; they also knew, to the last nickel, what they had bought for the money they had spent. Community relations were important—they'd learned that in business school —and so they retained Epstein to handle a minimum amount of polite publicity. "I'd make a bet," Epstein told me, "that Heath adds up the column inches of comment I get them and prorates my fees at so much an inch." After a preliminary look around their plant I was inclined to believe him. From machine shop to men's room, everything was tight and tidy.

I moved from office to office and floor to floor with Lewis at my elbow, wondering if I had bitten off more than I could chew. "Now this is our design department," said Lewis, ushering me through a door and looking at me expectantly. "Hmm," I said, "uh-huh." The design department, to a casual eye, looked painfully neat and enormously efficient. "Ah, yes," I added, nodding wisely. Lewis waited a moment or so for the questions I didn't ask and then closed the door and led me down the corridor. Another door, another weighty pause, another skeptical glance which meant okay, expert, start passing miracles. "Hmm," I said, and I hoped desperately that it sounded like a man whose keen brain was storing up impressions.

From the moment Lewis had called to say they had decided to—ah—avail themselves of my services my mind had been a blank. Gone was the brashness which had carried me through the conference. That had been a contest; a sparring match in which the object had been to win. Now the Gilbrick Company itself, the plant and the people, had taken on a sudden, solid reality and I was being paid to shape and change it and I didn't even know where to start.

"The records department is in here," said Lewis, opening still another door to reveal row upon row of gray-green filing cabinets. "If there's any information you need, you'll find them very cooperative."

"Ah, yes," I said. "Fine. Fine."

I hadn't seen one thing out of place, not one gum wrapper on the floor, not one water cooler which didn't work. The only recommendation I could give them was, "Carry on, boys, you're doing a swell job." And still Lewis plodded grimly onwards, guiding me through the personnel department and the company cafeteria and the accounting department and the production offices and ultimately to the factory floor itself where glistening machines chunk-chunked quietly to themselves, served by acolytes in spotless white coveralls. That was the end of the tour and Lewis took me back to his office where he settled into his leather swivel chair, took out his pipe and polished the bowl carefully with a handkerchief and then said, "Where would you like to begin?"

"I'll need an office," I told him, "or someplace reasonably private to work. I'll need a secretary, at least part-time. I can bring my own girl over, but it would be better to have one of yours, somebody who knows her way around the place." This was only partly bluff; I had already decided to hire a girl if they couldn't give me one. It would be worth the cost in terms of time saved on routine work. Lewis merely nodded, however, and made a note on his pad.

"We'll have them for you tomorrow morning," he said. "What else?"

"Access to any files I need, of course. I'll start with the records of your advertising for the past couple of years. The ads themselves, I mean, and the media and the schedules and so on. That's all for the first day or so. Then I'd like to get together with the same people who were at the conference, because I'll have some questions to ask. After that I may be after you or one of the others individually for more answers."

Lewis studied the sleek surface of his pipe. "Mr. Gilbrick," he said, "is a very busy man. He—ah—has to be out of the office a great deal of the time. The rest of us, of course, anything we can do . . ."

"Well . . ." I said briskly. I wanted desperately to dig into the job immediately, but I also needed time to think. "Well," I repeated standing up, "I'll see you in the morning then."

"Right," said Lewis. "We'll have everything set up for you." He opened the door of his office and stood beside it. As I walked down the long corridor toward the reception area I knew he was still standing there. I didn't look back, but I could feel his eyes on me.

Epstein had some words of reassurance.

"It's often like this at the beginning," he said. "I've been through it a dozen times. You have to remember that they do have a problem or they wouldn't have called you in. You *did* say their advertising wasn't too good . . ."

"If what you showed me is a fair sample, it's lousy."

"Okay, that means there's a monkey wrench someplace in all that lovely machinery. The toughest part of your job may be to find it. It may be some specific thing or person or it may be something so big and broad that a person standing close to it can't see it—an attitude, for example. It could be something they're proud of and you'll have a hell of a time unsticking them from it. Just start with those ads and work backward, sooner or later the whole picture will pop into your head."

Two telephone messages had come in while I was gone. One was from an employment agency and I rang them back, got the name of the company and set up an appointment for the earliest possible hour on the following Monday. The other was from Phil, who was apparently back in town after his latest sales swing. I called him also and thanked him again for the loan and told him how Cliff's difficulties had worked out.

"Bought that bottle of Scotch yet?" he asked.

"No," I answered, "but I just might do it this afternoon."

I did, too. I stopped at a liquor store near Grand Central and picked out a good brand and walked down to the train clutching the package as if it were an irreplaceable heirloom.

Janet met me at the station with the news that Cliff hadn't come home from school.

"Didn't you pick him up?" I asked, tossing my attaché case into the rear seat.

"I stopped by the school the way I always do and I couldn't find him. Skip was out front, but he didn't know where Cliff was. I thought he might have gotten a ride home with someone, but he still hasn't shown up."

I hoped he would be home by the time we arrived, but he wasn't. Not that there was anything ominous about a boy being a couple of hours late; I'd often stayed out until nightfall at Cliff's age. If he was just visiting a friend, fine, but these days when Cliff was out of sight he was very much in our minds.

"What are you supposed to do?" I asked. "Just what the hell are you supposed to do! 'Are you a responsible parent? Do you know where your teen-ager is at all times?' "—I was quoting from a recent article in a women's magazine.

"Don't ask me," said Janet. "I didn't write that."

"This lousy town has more cars in it than toilets and they expect you to keep track of kids. Short of chaining them up on the front lawn like goats or laying them out with a piece of lead pipe I don't know how the hell you're supposed to do it."

"I guess I'd better start telephoning," Janet said, but she had only made two calls when a car pulled up out front and Cliff walked in.

"Okay," I said, "where have you been?"

"Over to Joe's. He asked could I come over after school so I did. What's wrong with that?"

"Has Joe got a telephone?"

"Sure, Joe's got a telephone. Whatdaya think?" It crossed my mind briefly that my child had never heard of a family without a telephone, but that wasn't the point I wanted to make.

"Anything stopping you from phoning your mother and telling her where you were, so she wouldn't worry?"

A look of infinite weariness passed over his face.

"You're always treating me like a kid," he complained. "Anything I do—any little harmless thing like maybe stopping off to see someone—I get treated like a kid. I got some rights."

"Sit down on the sofa there," I told him.

"I got homework to do."

"So have I, so this won't take long. Just sit down."

I took a seat in the easy chair, opposite the sofa.

"Now, look, Cliff," I said. "This whole business is being treated as if it were an argument of some sort and it isn't. Nobody's trying to cage you up; we want you to see your friends and have as much fun as you can. It's not a question of whether you had a right to do something or not; calling your mother is a courtesy. I do it if I miss my train and I don't feel anyone's depriving me of my rights. People are going to expect this from you no matter where you go or how old you are. If you work at a job or live in a town, you're never going to get away from it so you may as well get used to it right now. We could lay off you, as you're always putting it, but the rest of the world won't. Now, doesn't that make some sense?"

"You'd think I didn't have any rights," he said.

I looked at Janet and she shrugged.

"Okay," I said, "you just concentrate on your rights. But don't be surprised if other people concentrate on theirs . . ."

I suppose ten thousand parents have said the same thing to ten thousand kids with about the same results. This isn't something you can be told, it's something you have to find out the hard way and that's the way youngsters have always learned. The difference, these days, lies in the fact that a kid may be too deeply in trouble to back out by the time he knows how the world whirls. Smashing a window is something you can live down, smashing a life isn't.

After dinner I sat down with a pen and a new notebook and started my Gilbrick file. I jotted down everything, every fact and every impression, no matter how routine or pointless it seemed. As Epstein said, the problem was in there someplace and if it had been obvious they would have seen it themselves. Most of the notes were brief—"File department, third floor, north corner. Miss Bloggins in charge. All files except accounting and confidential. Three employees." It didn't seem like much but it filled three pages of the notebook and it kept me busy until bedtime. "Gilbrick, Gilbrick, Gilbrick"; it was still circling around in my skull as I lay in

|159|

bed. But only one thought occurred to me and it was a very small thought which made me chuckle.

"Whazzat?" muttered Janet, half-asleep.

"Nothing," I said. "I'll tell you in the morning." I was thinking of Lewis arranging my working space and I made a private bet that it would be in a corner of the factory floor, someplace behind the drop hammers.

But I was wrong.

The place he found for me wasn't fancy, but it was comfortable and well-suited for my purposes, a quiet corner in the filing department with two windows and a roomy desk. He had picked a capable girl, too; a bright little bundle of bust and hair-do named Miss Mittle who stared at The Expert with awed brown eyes. The advertising files were on the desk; so was a company directory, a product list and assorted other scraps of information I would be likely to want.

"Okay?" said Lewis.

"Perfect. Couldn't be better."

"Well, I'll let you get started then," Lewis said, but he didn't leave. I opened the ad folder and riffled through the tear sheets inside. The ads I'd seen were there and so were others, some slightly better, perhaps, but all at the same general level and all pretty uninspiring. There was one possible exception: an odd little effort built around a cartoon character and a brief headline which was obviously meant to be punchy. I separated the sheet from the rest of the file and studied it. As an eye-catcher it didn't amount to much but somebody had made a try and that was intriguing.

"What do you think of them?" asked Lewis.

"Well . . . I'd like to study them before I say anything."

"You seemed positive enough at the meeting."

I grinned at him. "I was giving opinions then; anything I say now is a recommendation."

He took out his pipe and began polishing it.

"But you don't think much of them, do you?"

There was a problem here and it was one I knew I was going to have to climb over sooner or later. I had hoped it would be later, after I had put together some solid ideas and gotten to know my people better. It couldn't be helped, however, so I plunged right in.

|160|

"Who wrote them?"

"I did," Lewis replied, frowning at his pipe. "I wrote most of them. Other . . . ah . . . people handled a couple . . ." (that would probably be Gilbrick himself) ". . . and that cartoon thing you're holding, that was Junior's idea."

"Did it attract any attention?"

"No," said Lewis briefly. He pulled a tobacco pouch from his pocket and began loading his pipe, dropping small pinches of tobacco into the bowl and tamping each pinch down carefully. Oh, God, I thought, there's a whole damn story of some sort behind that and I'm going to have to pry it out. Meanwhile there was Lewis himself, who was probably a very bright guy and a first-rate executive, but as touchy as a schoolgirl about his literary abilities.

"Look," I said, "there's nothing wrong with the ads. They're well-written and they're good, but that's not the point. The point is whether they do what advertising is supposed to do and this is a very specialized business these days. A man could be a brilliant writer and still write . . . ah . . . inadequate ads."

"I see," said Lewis and Miss Mittle coughed. I had forgotten she was standing there and Lewis apparently had, too, because he gave her a startled glance and added, "Well, I must be getting to work." He marched off down the avenue of filing cabinets, his well-tailored back giving no clue to his reactions.

I sat there for a moment, tapping a pencil on the desk and revising an estimate of Mr. Lewis which obviously had been much too simple. He didn't like the whole idea, I was still sure of that. He didn't like it but he was going to handle it in his own way; he was going to allocate plenty of rope for me to hang myself. Nobody could claim later that I didn't have the firm's fullest cooperation and if, by some miracle, I actually did come up with something then Lewis was ready to settle for that. Quite a guy.

All I had to do was to produce that miracle.

I set Miss Mittle to work checking circulation figures—they should have been in the folders, but they weren't—and then I began to work my way through the individual ads, jotting down my comments on each one and the points it seemed to be trying to make. I was absorbed in this when Endicot, the production chief, came in and suggested lunch.

"Good God," I said, "is it that time already?"

"Quarter after twelve."

"Lunch time, Miss Mittle," I said. "Take off."

Endicot took me to the cafeteria, a democratically roomy place where everyone from executive to office boy seemed to eat. I spotted Junior at one table, in earnest conversation with a burly man in overalls, and Heath at another, with a fork in his right hand and a paperback thriller in the other. Evidently there were unseen depths in Heath, too.

Over soup and a sandwich, Endicot talked about the Gilbrick Company and its history. It wasn't the oldest firm in the field——"We can't put 1840 over the door, much as the Old Man would love to"—but it could point to a successful half-century. It wasn't necessarily the most conservative, either. "They have to be convinced something new is permanent," said Endicot. "Once they are, they're in with both feet. This building, for example. Took them ten years to decide they needed it. When they finally made up their minds, it went up in a hurry. How's the advertising look to you?"

It was the second time in four hours I had been asked that question and I was beginning to feel like a TV repairman, probing the interior of a set while the anxious family hung over his shoulder.

"I can't really say yet," I told him. "I want to take it apart and see what makes it tick. There won't be any fireworks for awhile yet. I sort of gathered," I added cautiously, "that . . . ah . . . people would prefer it that way."

"Oh, well; you know." He lifted the top of his sandwich and shot a glob of ketchup into it with one practiced jab of the bottle. "There was some argument about it. You probably guessed that when we took so long getting back to you. They want to do something, but they don't want to go overboard."

"What would you regard as going overboard?"

"Oh, well, you know," he said again. "Razz-ma-tazz and all that. Madison Avenue."

"Don't call it Madison Avenue," I answered. "Every business has its high pressure boys; your business has them, too."

"Oh, sure, sure, I know that." He grinned at me across the table. "I didn't mean to hit any sore spots."

"It's not a sore spot, it's just a practical point. It may be neces-

|162|

sary to brighten up your advertising, expand it a bit, put a little spirit, a little personality into it. I don't want people calling this razz-ma-tazz because we'll run into problems if they see it that way. You can take my word for it that I wouldn't recommend anything which would make Gilbrick look. . . ."

Endicot held up his hand.

"Hold it, hold it," he protested. "You don't have to sell me. The brighter the better, as far as I'm concerned. I said there was *some* concern about the possibility of going overboard, but that's only natural. Why, I can remember a time. . . ."

He launched into a long and very funny story about an experimental product of the 1930's which came to a lugubrious end and this led him into other reminiscences which took up the rest of the lunch hour. "When you get a moment," he said as we walked toward the door, "come around and let me give you a real tour of the plant." I told him I would.

By mid-afternoon, 3:30 or thereabouts, I had finished my rough notes on the ads. I turned them over to Miss Mittle for typing, put on my coat and went back to Epstein's office to see if there had been any letters or calls. The cupboard was pretty bare: a written confirmation of my appointment on Monday, a couple of ads and two bills, one for long-distance calls I had made on Epstein's phones and the other for some résumés I had had printed. Both amounts were relatively small, if I could call any amount small, but I regarded them with a certain wry amusement. Job Hunter, Inc., with its own offices, was now beginning to accumulate bills in its own right.

I was ready to head home at that point, but I didn't. I forced myself to sit down and type a couple of letters and begin the weekly revision of my "active list." That was the condition I had made with myself when I took on the Gilbrick assignment; there would be no letup in the search. Most of my time would be tied up, I knew that and I couldn't help it. I could avoid being lulled by the income and the activity. The letters had to go on circulating, the hot prospect list had to be kept up to date even if it meant hanging around the office until midnight.

I finished the letters by train time, however, and completed the list and a penciled draft of still another letter during the ride home.

|163|

Janet was standing on the platform looking grim and I wondered
for a moment if the kid had been kicking up trouble again, but he
hadn't. She was just very tired. The running battle with the boy
was tiring and so was the job with Max, which ceased to be any
fun in the spring when the suburban sailors started fitting out their
boats. This particular day, it seemed, had set something of a record and Janet's list of fellow townsmen who ought to be keel-
hauled had been expanded by a dozen names.

"Apparently," she said grimly as we drove away from the station,
"they can't put to sea safely without their cocktail flags. God, the
junk they're ordering. You know Whozit . . ."—I did know him
slightly as a face on the train—". . . well, he was in today, indent-
ing for damn near everything in the catalogue, including an echo-
sounder and a portable bar. He doesn't know what half of them
are for—except the bar, of course. When I think what we could do
with that money . . ."

"If it's any consolation to you," I told her, "he isn't buying anything with it."

"Are you crazy? If the Navy had half the equipment he's hung
on that boat we could lick any three nations in the world."

"I still say he isn't buying anything. Look, Epstein has a boat,
hasn't he? Now I'll make a bet that what he orders. . . ."

"Well, I can tell you what he ordered," Janet said. "Some paint,
some caulking compound, some rope and a new kedge. I handled
it."

"Okay, I can tell you the history of that boat. Epstein bought it
eight years ago after about a year of looking around to find something to suit him. He took the Coast Guard courses and the Yacht
Club's course in boat handling and he sat and listened to anyone
who could teach him something, never mind who they were. By
now he's pretty much of an expert and people treat him with a lot
of respect around the Yacht Club and that respect is what your
friend Whozit wants, only he wants to buy it out of the catalogue.
All that hardware is supposed to make him look salty."

"If he puts much more of it topside," said Janet, "he's going to
look upside down. That birdbath of his is going to roll right over
one of these days."

"I wouldn't worry. Give it a year and he'll sell the boat and start

|164|

after something else. Whozit's the great American buttonpusher. He's probably run through a dozen automated hobbies already and dropped them because he didn't get any fun out of them. He's always chasing something he can't catch up with and you really ought to feel sorry for him. A guy like Epstein, now; he doesn't give a damn whether he looks salty or not. He just loves boats."

"I'll feel sorry for him a year from now, then," said Janet. "Right now he gets on my nerves."

"He gets on everyone's nerves, but he happens to represent one hell of a market. He'll buy anything with a label that says 'Now you too can be an expert with one push of the button.' "

A car came rocketing up from the rear and I watched it for a moment while it swung into the left lane and shot past me with a resounding "vrooom" from twin exhausts.

"You know," I added, "I ought to confess something."

"What's that?"

"If somebody made a gadget with a label that said 'Now you too can straighten out companies with one push of the button,' I'd be standing in line to buy it."

If the button existed, however, I couldn't find it and I spent the next few days digging, digging, digging and bouncing questions off Lewis and Endicot and Heath. Why did they put more effort into certain cities? ("These have always been our best markets.") Why were company announcements mailed only to certain distributors? ("They've been with us a long time.") Had they ever discussed broadcast advertising? ("Too expensive.") Why had they redesigned one product two years before, another the previous year? ("We try to stay right on top of technical advances.") What was the thinking behind their packaging designs? Lewis raised his eyebrows at this question and answered, "I thought you were dealing with *advertising.*"

Fact by fact, the files mounted up and Miss Mittle's typewriter rattled along merrily, stopping only for lunch and the coffee breaks. The sales figures, analyzed month by month for a two-year period, told me only what I already knew: Gilbrick's sales had been rising steadily but they hadn't kept pace with the growth of the industry.

Gilbrick himself remained remote. I passed him occasionally in the corridors and was greeted with a jolly smile and a hearty, "How's it going?" The first time this happened I answered, "Fine ... ah ... by the way ..." and found myself talking to a retreating back. After that I simply said "Fine" or, to vary the monotony, "First rate."

I did trap Junior early in the second week and drag him off to the cafeteria for lunch. "Gee," he said, "I've been going to come back and see you but I figured you wouldn't want to be disturbed. Just starting out, I mean. She said you were sort of snowed under."

I deduced that "she" referred to Miss Mittle.

"I was hoping you would drop in," I told him. "I wanted to ask you about that ad; the one with the cartoon character."

"Oh, that," he said. He didn't seem very happy.

"It was your idea, wasn't it?"

"Well, yes. I guess you could say it was."

"What made you hit on that approach?"

"Well, now," said Junior, shifting in his chair uncomfortably. "It didn't work out very well, you know. It wasn't a very good idea."

"I know that. I'd still be interested in your reasons for trying it."

The question obviously raised embarrassing memories because he wriggled again and said, "Well ..." and then stopped.

"Well," he said again, "it's hard to know where to begin. I've always been interested in advertising, sort of, but I don't know very much about it. Still, when you look at a lot of the advertising that's going around these days and then you look at our ads. . . ."

"Yes, go ahead."

He gestured with one hand, nearly knocking over a water glass.

"Everyone kept saying what I wanted to do was funny advertising and that wasn't what I meant. Well, it *was* in a way, I suppose, only not really funny."

He took a deep breath and made another effort.

"All our ads were this stuff like, 'We make these products and they're the best quality products and if you're smart you'll buy them.' Well, I should have said before that whatever we did, I thought we ought to be doing a lot more. But then the way they were, they could be *anybody*. I mean, that's what we want to say, but it should be *us* saying it. But that doesn't mean funny, necessarily."

I took this apart in my head and did my best to reassemble it in some coherent order. "What you mean," I said finally, "is that you felt the ads should have some individuality."

"And ... and ... you know, brighter maybe. Not funny, that's what I kept trying to explain, just a little bit brighter."

"You wanted the ads to have some personality."

"*That's* it," said Junior. "Personality. Like somebody who's serious ... I mean takes his work seriously but he's pleasant, too. A serious explanation in a pleasant way. He doesn't take *himself* too seriously."

"So what happened?" I already had a pretty good idea.

"Well, you know, I kept bringing this up and finally I got an okay to go ahead and do one. So I wrote some copy and we got a guy to do the cartoon and we ran it. But nothing much happened. Nobody said they didn't like it, you understand, but nobody said they did either. It just didn't stir up any comment at all and of course it should have. It was different, I mean, even if it wasn't any good."

"I've got to get back to work," I said, "but I wish you would drop around. Just come around anytime."

"Of course, if I could help any ..." he said hopefully.

"I think there's a good chance you could," I told him, "especially when we get things shaped up."

Junior's little tragedy had been enlightening; behind it I could see Lewis and his "enough rope" tactic. The kid's instincts had put him on the right track, there was no doubt of that, but he obviously didn't realize that one little ad with very limited circulation would be swallowed up in the chaos of the marketplace. I went back to my office and took his ad out of the folder and studied it again. He was groping for that elusive thing called personality, you could see that, but he just hadn't touched it. As the starting point for a whole campaign, it might have had possibilities. As a one-shot proposition it didn't stand a chance.

Beyond these technicalities, Junior had put his hoof squarely into the trap I was carefully skirting. Brightening the ads was a breeze; any competent copywriter could do it. Selling a smile to people whose dignity depended on a frown was something else

|167|

again and that phrase "hyping up" hovered over the whole business.

I dug into the stack of paper again and Miss Mittle phoned the stockroom for a new typewriter ribbon.

Away from the Gilbrick plant, in the Automat and Epstein's office, on the train and at home, I spent a lot of time just sitting and staring at nothing. I wanted desperately to be back at the agency again and to run some of my questions through one of the old-time brain-storming sessions. It wasn't the answers I needed; I knew I could find those myself. It wasn't even the confidence which came from spreading the responsibility; I'd learned to get by without that. It was the sense of proportion you gain from the group's reactions, the knowledge of what the word "good" really means or the word "bad" or such words as "important" and "trivial," "reality" and "illusion." Day by day, problem by problem, I might be drifting away from reality without knowing it and yet there was nobody I could talk to, not Phil, not the boys at the Automat, not Janet, not even Epstein, about the facts I had pulled from the Gilbrick files. Once, during the war, I had become separated from my patrol for a few panic-stricken minutes in the trackless and hostile desert; another time, just after the war, I had lived in a cheap furnished room and worked among strangers in a strange city, and yet I had never been so alone as I was when I sat at the desk beyond the file cabinets and stared at those words "good" and "bad" and tried to understand what they meant.

I was tired, too; I was very tired and this didn't make things any easier. It's an unpleasant surprise, as I've said, to find out that being jobless costs money; it's an even rougher shock to learn that you have to work at being unemployed and work hard. I was on the go constantly now, jumping from home to Epstein's office to the Gilbrick plant to the employment agencies to job interviews to hurried lunches; wrenching my mind around to each new situation, pounding out letters, stuffing résumés in envelopes, squinting at help-wanted columns and dredging, dredging, dredging through the Gilbrick records. There was a week of whirling confusion when one interview went unexpectedly well. "It looks like we might fit you in," they said. "You'll be hearing from us." What did I do now; try to stall them? Try to rush the Gilbrick work? Walk out on Gilbrick? Lose out on the offer? I sweated through that week and this took its emotional toll, but I never heard from them again. And then there were sudden moments of premonition during the day, those vague, uneasy hunches that something else had gone wrong at home. I boarded the train every evening with a knot in my stomach which often relaxed into nausea when I found everything was okay.

But there was some progress, too. The Gilbrick picture was growing clearer now and the missing pieces were beginning to be evident. The firm's relationship with its retailers was puzzling, for example. It seemed solid enough and there were no problems in the files and that was just the trouble—there should have been. There should have been a lot of items in the files which weren't there—records of mailings, echoes of misunderstandings, copies of correspondence dealing with this question or that complaint. I knew who the retailers were and what products they handled and how many units they usually sold but that was virtually all I knew. No personalities climbed out of the file folders, no Mr. X in Dayton wrote purple-faced, sputtering letters, no Mr. Y in Tucson offered wry, tanned, ten-gallon comments. Who were these people?

"*Who* are they?" repeated Lewis, raising one eyebrow. "Regional businessmen, of course. Well-established firms, you can count on that."

"How long since you've visited any of them?"

"Well, the schedule varies from market to market, of course, but on an average our salesmen drop in about. . . ."

"No, not your salesmen. *You,* personally." Both eyebrows went up this time, but I went on doggedly. "Take this one over in Jersey, for example. Weber, Inc. According to this, old man Weber died—let's see—about two years ago. Daughter took over . . . uh . . . Mrs. Tracy. Now has anyone here apart from the sales staff ever met Mrs. Tracy?"

"Not to my knowledge," said Lewis. He was wearing an I-knew-he'd-do-something-crazy-and-now-he's-done-it expression, but he was interested, too. He wanted to see where all this was leading.

"Then I suggest that I visit her, along with somebody from the management."

"Just what do you expect to find? And what does all this have to do with advertising?"

"Answer to your first question: it's what I expect *not* to find. Answer to the second: it could have a lot to do with advertising, but I'd rather go into that later. Whoever goes with me, however, I think there's a good chance we might want him to carry on and make some more calls to other retailers by himself."

"Well," said Lewis, "you're the expert. If you really think it's vital to call on Mrs. . . . ah. . . ."

"Tracy."

". . . to call on Mrs. Tracy, by all means go ahead. But I'm sure I don't know who could go with you."

"I could suggest somebody."

"Who's that?" asked Lewis. He obviously thought I meant him. "Junior."

"Junior! Now just what in. . . ."

"Well, let me know," I said.

"Junior," he repeated, and I went back to my office figuring that was that. An hour or so later, however, he phoned me and gave the go-ahead. I could guess that the matter had been bounced off the Big G, who had decided it might be nice for Sonny to get out in the sunshine so long as he had a responsible adult along with him. The day was still young so I scooped up Junior and cleared out before they could change their minds. I didn't phone Mrs. Tracy to let her know we were coming. I wanted to see her in her natural habitat.

Junior was tickled pink to be going out on an ambulance call. He battered me with questions through the hour and a half trip and I fended them all off. "You're asking the wrong person," I told him. "Just hang on until you can try them on Madame Tracy. Then it just could happen that all will be made clear."

It was a big place for that area, an imposing three-story building at the heart of a shopping center with "Weber & Tracy" in gold letters across the front. Either some Weber still had a hand in the business or she had hung onto her father's name as a mark of respect. We located the office easily—it was at the rear of the ground floor—but I stopped Junior as he put his hand on the doorknob.

"Hold it," I said. "You've got a small chore to take care of first."

"What's that?"

"Have a look around see if you can locate a Gilbrick product."

He was off like a bird dog and a full ten minutes went by before

|170|

he returned. Something like comprehension was beginning to dawn on his face.

"Find it okay?" I asked.

"No, not by myself. I finally had to ask a salesgirl and she wasn't sure. She asked a guy who was there and he *said*—like this—'Oh, it's over in the corner someplace.' He said it like that, sort of offhand. So I went over and it's there, all right, only the way they've got those other displays stacked up you can't see it unless you're right on top of it. I walked right past it, first time."

"Okay," I told him, "that answers two questions."

"Which two?"

"What sort of break do Gilbrick products get? Answer, lousy. How much do the sales people push Gilbrick products? Answer, they don't. Now let's call on Mrs. T."

We found her behind a cluttered desk, a brisk, black-haired girl who could be called pretty and who was much younger than I had expected. "Yes?" she said, without glancing up.

"We're from the Gilbrick Company," I explained. "This is. . . ."

"You're early. We always reorder at the end of the month." She scribbled her signature on a letter and then raised her eyes. "Oh," she said, "you're a different man. The other man was here a week —ten days ago; maybe he didn't tell you."

"We're not salesmen," I told her. "This is Mr. Gilbrick, Jr., assistant to the president of the company, and I'm a special consultant."

"Good God, what are you doing over here?" She pushed back her chair and looked Junior up and down. "Now look," she added, "if you've come to raise some sort of hell. . . ."

"No, no, no, this is a . . . educational tour. I'd be interested in knowing, for example, why Gilbrick's display has been shoved off in a corner."

She eyed me warily.

"That's an honest question," I added. "We really do want to know."

"Okay, you asked for it." She leaned back in her chair. "It's good quality stuff, the best I carry. . . ."

Junior beamed.

"And there's a steady demand for it. Loyal following, you might say. Always has been; probably always will be. . . ."

Junior nodded.

"Apart from that—nothing."

She spread her hands apart, palms upward, and I waited.

"Nothing?" said Junior finally, "I'm afraid I. . . ."

"Nothing," she repeated firmly. "Nothing more to say. Sells just as well off in the corner as it would in the middle of the center aisle. I'm short of floor space; I'm short of counter space. . . ."

"I know," I told her.

"Do you really? Have you ever tried to find room for all the different brands there are these days and still have an attractive looking floor and leave plenty of room for customers to circulate and organize the whole works so a salesgirl who can hardly spell her own name can lay her hand on the right box?" She shook her head. "Oh, brother!" she added.

"Well, look," said Junior, "If our products are good . . . I mean what else . . . ?"

That set her off and she began talking and Junior sat there, taking it all in. She concentrated on him—the name had obviously made its impression—and I slipped a notebook out of my jacket pocket and quietly jotted down some of the main points. What was Gilbrick doing about displays? There hadn't been a new one "since the Civil War." Why did Gilbrick ignore the sales clerks? She flourished a booklet sent by another firm, a simple Question and Answer description of their product. Where was Gilbrick's advertising, its *real* advertising? Junior opened his mouth and closed it again. He was beginning to see the point. What about Gilbrick's new products? They were fine when they came, but she never knew when they were coming. What about packaging, what about premiums; she went on for another twenty minutes or so before she finally ran down. "What it adds up to," she finally said, "is just this. The product is swell but you just can't compete in anything else and these days that's just about everything else."

Junior was very apologetic and slightly appalled. "Well," he said, "what we'll have to do . . ." I stepped on his foot and thanked Mrs. Tracy politely and hustled the kid out of the office before he could make any commitments.

"Boy," he sighed when we got outside. "I just never . . . Was all that true, what she was saying?"

"My guess would be that most of it was," I answered. "She was

|172|

pretty wound up, of course, and she probably went in for a lot of exaggeration. The main point is that she's been bottling it up for two years and this is the first chance she's had to uncork it to anyone higher than the salesman who drops in once a month to pick up the reorder."

"Well, *he* should have reported something," said Junior indignantly.

"Why should he? Who ever encouraged him to? He's got a good account there and a regular reorder; why should he be the one to rock the boat when nobody else cares?"

"Yeah, I guess," said Junior.

I kept the results of our trip under cover for the time being and drew up a list of retailers for Junior to visit in a two-state area. Lewis okayed the project with a wry smile and a single comment: "In due course, I suppose, the rabbit will come out of the hat." Off went the kid, Special Agent X in a perky red sports car, and his first report came in two days later. After that they came in regularly, the early ones rambling and disorganized, the later ones briefer but more searching and more to the point. He was learning and you could watch him learn with each successive envelope. Some of the retailers were cheerful, some were sour, most echoed Mrs. Tracy's candid views. Junior's reports on displays were most illuminating; I copied them out on a separate sheet because they summed up the situation at a glance.

Meanwhile, I was digging into other areas and piling up other evidence. I plowed through the reference books on Epstein's shelves and at the public library and in the offices of newspapers and trade magazines, pulling out up-to-date circulation and market figures and matching them against Gilbrick's planning for the past few years. It was sensible planning as far as it went but most of it could be summed up in that old wartime phrase—too little and too late. One afternoon I polished off the last file folder and stacked the whole works together and called it finished. If it was humanly possible to be sure about anything, I was sure I had found the answer.

"The Only Man Who Ever Labored Ten Hours a Day to Be a Bum"

It's funny the way these things go. You work for weeks and in the end you come back to the starting point and an answer which is almost a cliche, but you have to do it that way because you have to be positive. There was nothing particularly mysterious about the Gilbrick Company's problems, it had simply lost touch with its customers. The still, small voice of quality is often shouted down in the marketplace: Gilbrick's products were up to date, but not its method of selling them.

I spent several days writing my report. It covered a half-dozen different areas and each area was broken down into the facts I had uncovered, the conclusions to be drawn from those facts and my recommendations. There was a page of estimates to go with the recommendations and finally there was a summary, the briefest one I could write, which led off the report and gave the principal points at a glance. It was a thick report, the size of a young novel, and a good one and I was very proud of it. Looking at it as honestly as I possibly could, I felt it was one of the best pieces of work I had ever turned out.

There was nothing particularly brilliant in the report; there was no magic formula, no catchphrase to sweep the nation, no piece of planning which would make a million dollars overnight. But there was no hedging in it, either. There was no point which had been skimmed over, no "insurance" to protect the planner if the recommendations didn't pan out. It was thorough because I had put a lot of work into it and it was candid because I had nothing to lose.

There was always the off-chance that it was good enough to get me a permanent job, but I was too seasoned in the strange psychology of job-hunting to expect this. People may admire their psychiatrists, but they seldom marry them. In many cases, the main value of a consultant lies in the fact that he *is* an outsider; he can take short cuts without shattering protocol and he can push for results without raising disturbing suspicions that he may be after somebody's job. As an associate of some sort—an account executive in their agency, perhaps—they might be happy to work with me, but taking me into their circle was another matter.

Handing over the report and leading the Gilbrick people through it, point by point, took a half-dozen meetings and when it was finally wrapped up I had fitted the last piece of the puzzle into place. They were a bit stunned, I think, by its size and by the interweaving of advertising and sales promotion and packaging and relations with retailers. All these areas and others had been only casually related in their previous operations and this, of course, had been one of their problems.

Lewis supported most of my recommendations. The whole, complicated structure went far beyond the mere "hyping up" he had feared and if he felt a bit silly he was man enough not to show it. Heath supported them, too, somewhat to my surprise. I'll never know what sold him but it could have been the obvious inefficiency of their previous, low-budget program. Junior and Endicot had been reformers from the first and the only remaining problem lay with Gilbrick himself, who came down out of his tree-house to hem and haw and ask if there wasn't some way they could get these results without committing themselves to any actual changes. I saw the picture clearly now, for they were all men of sufficient wisdom but their leader was one of the great American buttonpushers. If he went into cold water at all he had to go in inch-by-inch, and inch-by-inch through that week the rest of them pushed him in.

They raised their advertising and promotion budget by a substantial amount and lined up a good, small agency. They hired another consultant to revamp their packaging—that had been one of my recommendations—and they appointed a marketing manager —that had been another. I kept my mouth shut until they asked for my opinion and then I suggested Lewis for the job with Junior as his assistant. Lewis said okay and promptly turned a major portion of the responsibility over to Junior, which was what I had hoped he would do. This provoked the last little rebellion from the head of the table and Endicot put it down with a firm hand. "God dammit, Gilbrick," he said. "Give the kid a break. He deserves a promotion sometimes, you know, even if he is the boss's son."

And that was the end of the Gilbrick assignment.

I went back to the offices of Job Hunter, Inc., with a check and a letter of appreciation, signed by Gilbrick and undoubtedly written by Lewis. I felt I had earned both. As the boys at the Automat had predicted, I had served as hand holder, field worker, management organizer, messenger, and family councilor, and the technicalities of advertising had played a relatively small part. I was happy and I was temporarily solvent, but I was still unemployed and I was very, very tired, so tired that the only thing I could think of was the last thing I had any right to think of, and that was how wonderful it would be to take a vacation.

One of my first acts was to repay Phil's $500.

"Why don't you hang on to it?" he said. "You may still need it."

"Then I'll borrow it back again. This money went for a dead horse and I'd like to clean it up. The next time I borrow anything it will be to buy food or pay the mortgage."

"Okay," he said reluctantly, putting the check in his wallet. "But remember it's here if you need it."

Phil was getting increasingly restless in his job. There were too many memos, he told me, too many meetings, too little actual selling.

"For God's sake, Phil," I said, "don't just sit there until they toss you out like an old toothpaste tube. You don't want to end up like me."

"Don't worry," he told me. "I'm looking. As a matter of fact . . ." he grinned at me ". . . I'm always looking. These days— what's that line about anchors?"

"Having an anchor to windward?"

"That's the one. It pays—as you know."

I shoved the rest of the money into the bank, except for a few dollars which I kept out to buy a model airplane kit for Skip, a couple of additional road-racing cars for Cliff and a bottle of Scotch for Janet and myself. It was a nice feeling, paying off a debt and putting some money into the bank, and for a few days I wondered if acting as a consultant might not be turned into a permanent career.

"Well, yes," said Epstein doubtfully, when I mentioned this idea to him. "Provided you know what you're getting into. I wouldn't take the Gilbrick job as typical if I were you. It was a pretty specialized thing and you're not likely to run into something of the sort very often. Don't forget that you'd have to spend a lot of time selling your services and you'd have to find some way to do this and still keep on providing them. And then they don't come along one after the other, you know; you could go six months without lining up anything and then get three at once and have to turn two down. The best thing, if you're going to try it, is to have an independent income of some sort . . ."

I said I'd work on that.

It was surprising how quickly the Gilbrick Company slid into the past. I knew more about its inner machinery than any of its employees, more than some of its executives, and yet I had never really been a part of the company, not even for a few weeks. The table at the Automat was far more familiar but when I returned there I found even that had changed. The luncheon circle had dwindled by a few more faces and the oilman had gone.

"Real estate, can you imagine that?" asked Les, who was eating alone. "He landed a job with a real estate firm."

"It follows, in a rough sort of way," I said. "Oil leases and so on, I mean. How are you doing?"

Les was doing just about the same, but he was working on something. It was something different, something big. He couldn't talk about it but if it did come through . . .

"I hate to be a wet blanket," I said, "but you were the one that told me . . ."

"No, no, no, this isn't like that at all. It could fall through, of course—I'm ready for that—but, believe me, it isn't any runaround. It's the real thing."

The Job Hunter: The Diary
of a "Lost" Year

I kept my fingers crossed for him. You can know this game from A to Z and every trick and twist and angle in it, and hope can still make a sucker out of you.

I still felt tired and I couldn't seem to shake it off. I'll feel better, I thought, when the effects of all that high-pressure pushing wear off, but the days slipped by and they didn't. I took a three-day weekend but this didn't help much either and my eagerness to line up interviews gradually became a reluctance. Putting on a clean shirt and a freshly pressed tie, wiping the dust off my shoes, packing my attaché case, climbing on to the bus, pasting on a smile and skirmishing with the receptionist and fencing with her boss and saying "thank you" and coming away with the knowledge of another trip wasted, another dollar gone; all this became drudgery. Claustrophobia drove me out of my cubicle and anxiety drove me back in. I needed some part of the hope which was driving Les, even if it was a false hope which would end only in another defeat.

The lists and the letters, the letters and the lists; I grew so sick of them one morning that I almost heaved the whole works into the wastebasket. "Pentland, Inc., B. J. Miller, adv. mgr. Interviewed Mar. 18. Followup calls Mar. 30, Apr. 6 . . ." and so on and so on, page after page of them, scribbled over, check-marked, crossed out with the big red X which meant the lead was dead beyond all possible doubt. Tired, tired; God, I never knew you could be so tired. The names began to blur and swim under my eyes and the lines on the notebook page moved and flowed upward, oddly like a picket fence rising into the air. People were rushing back and forth in the corridor and shouting and I wanted them to stop but they all came into the cubicle instead: Miss Mittle wearing a bathing suit and Lewis riding a bicycle and the little round man from the employment agency carrying a basket of apples and Abbott and Costello and Miss Halley and they all pointed at me and began laughing and laughing and laughing. It was so cold in the cubicle and so dark and a white mist was drifting around the huge Victorian mirror with the gilt vine leaves around the frame and the leering, obscene Cupid sprawled across the top. I mustn't look into the mirror, I knew that and they'd warned me not to, but I looked anyway and I saw a clown's face, death-white and blood-red with huge circles around the eyes and thick rubbery lips twisted upwards in an imbecile grin and when I touched my cheek it cracked and fell away and there was nothing behind it but a revolting mass of corruption and I began screaming, but the bell was tolling, the bell, the bell, the bell . . .

I woke up with a violent start and sat for a few seconds with the sweat on my forehead and the horror of the dream still surrounding me. The bell went on ringing, the shrill bell, the telephone bell. I reached for the phone and knocked the receiver off its cradle and picked it up from the desk and said, "Yes?"

"I'm not sure I've got the right party," said a cheerful but puzzled voice, "This is Ed Cunelli."

Yes, of course, it was . . . uh . . .

"You were out to see us about a month ago," said the voice helpfully and the fog cleared. It was the man who had mentioned the award, the "manager" from the plant I had had so much trouble finding. "Oh, yes," I said. "How are you?"

"Now, look," said the voice briskly, "there may not be anything in this, but we do some subcontracting for an outfit that's spreading like crabgrass. They're interested in finding a couple of people and they're asking around and I told them a guy had been in to see me recently—that's you, you understand . . ."

"Yes, of course."

"I told them a guy had been in to see me recently that might . . . Of course, I don't know if you're still available."

"Well . . . uh . . . yes, yes I am."

"Maybe you'd want to follow this up then."

"I would like to, yes."

"Well, I read them part of your résumé over the phone and they sounded interested, so it might be worth your time. The man to call . . . got a pencil and paper?"

I took down the name and address—it was also in the suburbs— and read them back to him.

"That's got it," he said. "They're expecting to hear from you, so just give them a shout and mention my name. You'll find they're easy to talk to."

"I'll do that," I said. "And thanks—thanks so much. I'm very grateful."

"Don't mention it," replied the cheerful voice. "They're customers, you know; I like to do them a favor now and then if I can. Good luck."

I remembered, after I hung up, that one of the big, red X's in my notebook lay across this man's name. No lead, apparently, could be called dead beyond any possible doubt.

Well, here we go again.

I called this new prospect and set up a meeting for the following day, an arrangement which cheered me up slightly. A quick appointment can be a good sign; it may just mean that they have a genuine opening and mean to fill it without any fooling around. I was entering the name in my notebook when Les phoned to ask if I was going to meet him at the Automat.

"You sound excited," I said. "Did it come through?"

"Yes, yes, it did. I'll tell you all about it when I see you."

Poor Les, he had been on the bricks—I did some quick addition in my head—for something like fifteen months now, not much short of a year and a half. Whatever he had found, I hoped it was good and I hoped it was permanent.

I started work on a letter but my eyelids were getting heavy again, so I put on my hat and went out for a walk before lunchtime. This perpetual drowsiness would have to be shaken off somehow; it would get me off to a poor start if I ever did land a job. I walked up the avenue a few blocks, stopping at an occasional shop window, and then cut cross-town and down again to the Automat. Les was sitting at a table for two by the window and he had draped his coat over the other chair to save it. "Go get your lunch," he said, "and I'll fill you in while we're eating."

"Now then," I said, after I'd collected a sandwich and a cup of coffee, "what is it, where is it—what's the story?"

"Well," he answered, "to begin at the beginning—no, it really started before that . . ."

I bit into my sandwich and waited.

"Well," he said again, "it actually came up about three months ago. It was in a magazine—an ad, I mean—and I didn't pay any attention to it at first, of course, but then I got to thinking and I thought what the hell, why not?"

He paused at this point and looked at me, so I said, "Sure, why not?"

"Well, that's the way I figured it. So we wrote a couple of letters back and forth and then he wrote—this vice-president—and said he'd be passing through New York in a few weeks and could we get together. So I said okay, figuring if I'd already landed something by that time there'd be no harm done and if I hadn't this would be one in the bank."

"Makes sense," I said.

"So, anyway, he was here for about a week and we had three or four talks—there were a lot of things which had to be sorted out and there was a lot of thinking—a *hell* of a lot of thinking—which I had to do. Then we traded a couple of more letters and that was it. It's all set."

"Dammit, what's the job?"

"Oh, I thought I told you. I'm to be a sort of administrative director. The point is that they do a lot of business back here and with my background *here,* plus my experience—it all fits together, you see."

"Les," I said. "Where is this job?"

"Australia."

"*Australia!* But . . . how long will you be there?"

"Permanently, if the job works out. Maybe even if it doesn't."

"You mean," I said, "that you'd . . . you'd emigrate there? For good?"

"Well, why not?" he answered. He stared through the window at the city outside. "I thought it all out; believe me I thought it all out and it makes sense. A man has ability, he has experience, he has twenty-five—maybe thirty good years still ahead of him. Why waste it all hanging around where you aren't needed when they can use you someplace else?"

"Yes . . . but . . ."

"You sound like it's something strange," Les said. "People pulled up their stakes and came here, you know. Your family did, my family did, millions of others did. I'm just doing the same thing, that's all."

"Sure, but look what they were leaving!"

"Look what I'm leaving," said Les, bitterly, "just look at it. Forget about the world of the four-color ad for a moment and take a good look at the reality. Look at the streets you don't dare walk on at night; look at the communities where nobody can do anything different or say anything different. Look at all the things

|181|

which ought to be talked about and all the people who are afraid
to talk about them . . ."

It was like lifting the lid of a candy box and finding a gun inside.
This was Les talking, the irrepressible Les who rolled with the
punches.

". . . look at the management that doesn't manage and the lead-
ership that doesn't lead," he continued. "Look at the degenerate,
sadistic filth on every newsstand and the nice respectable people
buying chocolate bars a few feet away and pretending they don't
see it because if they did see it they'd have to do something about
it . . ."

"Yes, but . . ."

The old grin came back. "When your ancestors decided to cross
the ocean, I'll bet there were people who said, 'Yes, but . . .' "

"Well, I suppose . . ."

"And 'the grass isn't always greener' and 'you can't lick a problem by running away from it.' And those people were right, too;
you want to remember that. But your grandparents decided to come
anyway and they knew a lot less about what they were getting into
than I do."

"Les," I said, "it's your life. This is the sort of decision you
have to make for yourself."

"But you think I'm wrong?"

"I think everything you've said is right—as far as it goes. But
I'm just wondering if you aren't letting a handful of fools and de-
generates run you out of your country. Hell, Les, you don't have to
be a job hunter to run up against this; they throw *customers* out of
their stores. Like every slob that ever came into a few bucks, they
push people around while they have it and they'll start whining
when it runs out. You've been making the same rounds I have,
Les; you know you've met ten decent, responsible people for every
one idiot. And the same percentage holds for the crime situation,
believe me. These . . . these twisted animals are only a tiny minority."

"They've always been only a tiny minority; any time, any place.
But the vast majority is letting them decide who has a right to walk
down the street—or go on living—and who hasn't. If your vast
majority doesn't speak up pretty soon it'll be too late. And I, for

|182|

one, am not going to stick around to find out whether they finally find the guts to do it. It's a funny thing," Les added, "I always used to wonder when I was a kid what that phrase meant—throwing away your birthright for a mess of pottage. Now I know. I hope I'm wrong, you must understand that; I want with all my heart to be wrong. But I don't think I am. To borrow a phrase: never before have so many thrown away so much for so little."

"When are you leaving?" I asked.

"The end of next week; next Friday. This is the last time I'll be in here," he added. "There's all the packing and subletting the apartment and a million other things. That's why I was hoping you could make it today, because I won't be seeing you again."

"You'll keep in touch, won't you?" I said. "I think we'll probably be moving, but the guy I've borrowed an office from—Epstein—he'll know where I am."

I wrote the address on a paper napkin, and he put it in his wallet.

"Do you remember when I first found you fumbling around in the corridor at that employment agency? It seems like a long time ago, doesn't it?"

"I remember," I said, "and thanks for everything, Les."

"That's okay; don't forget that somebody had to show me the ropes. I'll leave the round table in your hands; do what you can for the new boys."

"I'll do that, Les. So long and good luck."

"So long, cobber," he said. I watched him walk through the door and I knew that something had been lost forever, though what it was and who had lost it I couldn't be sure.

"Ya through wit' these plates?" asked the girl who was clearing the tables.

There was a job to do that afternoon, the routine research for the interview the following day. The second-hand magazine shop was closest to the Automat, so I went there first. My next stop was the office, to check Epstein's reference shelves and then the public library for the books he didn't happen to have. Epstein's collection of books was useful, but it also was small and rather specialized. I worked at the library until four o'clock, which left me just enough time to return to the office and make a few discreet

|183|

phone calls to Phil and a couple of other friends who might be able to fill out the picture. At a preliminary glance the picture looked encouraging. Phil had heard of the company and was slightly surprised that I hadn't. "They're small," he said, "but they're coming along fast. I don't know anything about them personally—I've never done any business with them—but everything I've ever heard about them is favorable." So far, so good; I shoved my notes and the magazines I had purchased into the attaché case for closer study at home.

Janet was feeling edgy that evening and said, "Oh, God," when I dumped the files out on the dining room table.

"It's got to be done," I told her. "You used to go dancing around the place when I got a lead. 'Oh, boy; oh, boy; oh, boy'— remember? So now it's 'oh, God.' "

"What is it this time?" she asked and I showed her one of the ads. "Doesn't look bad," I said.

"Good or bad, you put in hours of work on these things two or three evenings a week and the next day some guy shakes his head and it all goes down the drain. That's why I said 'Oh, God'; do we really have to go to all this trouble just to be turned down?"

"My love," I told her, "you probably married the only man in history who ever labored ten hours a day to be a bum. Most men can achieve it just by sitting down. But I've got all this stuff together and I may as well look it over."

I liked the ads. They were strong and straightforward; messages from people who knew what they were talking about and who they were talking to. It was obviously a firm that, in Cunelli's phrase, had its customers sitting right in its lap. The information I had culled from the reference books was good, but not exciting; it was a smallish company and, so far as I could tell from checking cross-references, it was under firm and intelligent direction. I decided that these were no-nonsense people and that a plain necktie and a candid manner would be the best tactic.

It was another one of those one-train-into-the-city, another-train-out deals, so I was able to grab a half an hour at the office. There was no mail and only one phone call which had baffled Epstein's switchboard girl. "It was somebody called Les," she said, wrinkling her forehead. "He didn't give any other name and he left the funniest message. I've got it here someplace . . . oh, here we are:

'Forgot . . . to . . . ask.   Shall . . . I . . . look . . . around . . . for . . .
something . . . for . . . you . . . when . . . I . . . get . . . there?   Good
. . . luck . . . copper.' "

"That's 'cobber,' " I told her.

"I don't know what it means, but it sounds dirty."

"It isn't," I said. "He's just practicing something. If he calls
again, tell him 'Thanks, but no thanks.' "

"That doesn't make sense, either," she complained, but she
wrote it down.

The train ride out of the city was as dreary as ever; a sooty,
jerky trip through suburbs in which old houses with character but
no paint rubbed shutters with boxy new subdevelopments which
had paint but no character. I found the place with no trouble this
time; it was located on a main highway only a short bus ride from
the station.

"Kevenski, marketing director" was the name in my notebook
and Kevenski, the marketing director, turned out to be an amiable
but very businesslike guy who took my résumé, read it through
once, went back to the beginning and read it through again and
then proceeded to lead me through it, paragraph by paragraph and
line by line. I produced my letter from Gilbrick, but refused to talk
about the work. If he wanted to call Lewis, I said, he was welcome
to do so and Lewis could decide how much information he wanted
to let out. "Not important," said Kevenski, airily. "Let it go." I was
pretty sure he would call Lewis if things got at all serious.

It wasn't the interview which depressed me, it was the fact that
Kevenski handed me over to their personnel manager, a guy
named Donnell, for another interview after lunch. As far as I was
concerned this was the beginning of the end but I had made the
trip out there and I might as well see it through. I ate lunch at a
diner across the street and squandered a handful of coins on a call
to Epstein's secretary, who had nothing to report.

Donnell was equally pleasant, equally professional, but the term
"personnel manager" chilled me. I could see "personality tests"
looming on the horizon and I was damned if I was going to take
them. This second interview, however, turned out to be fairly brief.
Donnell also led me through my résumé—his questions were less
technical and more personal—and then surprised me by suggesting
a tour of the plant. I peered into offices and admired machines and

|185|

shook hands with a dozen people whose names I didn't catch and it was the Gilbrick tour all over again, with another Lewis at my elbow, watching my reactions. "Ah, yes," I said on one floor, and "uh-huh, yes, very interesting" on another. When we had finished the sightseeing Donnell parked me in his office and disappeared for about fifteen minutes and then came back and asked if I could see their Mr. Baxter the following day.

"Well, I . . ."

"Mr. Baxter's our general manager," he added firmly. "I've set up an appointment for you at 11:30, if that's all right. It was very nice to have met you."

I got back to Grand Central with just enough margin to catch my regular train and I blew hot and cold on the whole business all the way home.

"Well, why not?" asked Janet. "What can you lose?"

"The round trip fare, another full day, the chance of another lead if somebody should call up while I'm out of the office. I'm not going to land this."

"It's up to you," she said. "But I think I'd take a chance. You're just discouraged."

"Okay," I answered, "I'll try it."

But I changed my mind on the way to the city the next morning. I was tired and I was broke and I wanted to get my turn-downs in one trip. Walking through Grand Central I reached a compromise. If there was anything else cooking when I reached the office I'd call up and cancel the date with Baxter. If there wasn't, I'd go.

"Nothing," said Epstein's girl. "No mail, no calls yet this morning. It's early yet, though; something might come in."

"I hope it doesn't," I told her. "I'm going to be out most of the day."

Baxter was a big man, not necessarily fat but just big, with big hands and a big neck and a massive, craggy face topped by a shock of black-gray hair. The résumé was on his desk—I would have bet on that—and he marched me through it yet another time. There was one slight difference this time; most of Baxter's questions took the form of comments. "Interesting work, hey?"—he was talking about copywriting—or "lot of angles to that one, hey?" Finally he laid the résumé on his desk and looked at the ceiling and said ab-

|186|

ruptly, "You don't know much about this business, do you?"

The question implied that he had already accepted the answer so I simply said "No."

"Well, then," he added, standing up suddenly. "Let's have some lunch."

We went to the diner across the street.

"The food here is lousy," he commented, wedging himself into a plastic-upholstered booth with some difficulty. "But I like a change from the company cafeteria. Have a menu. I don't recommend *anything*, but the spaghetti's usually harmless. You didn't happen to see that thing on television last night about the . . ."

He talked trivia until the spaghetti came and then, with no perceptible change in tone, he began talking about his company. It was not what you'd call an old company, but it did date back to the end of the war. "Hard to realize it's such a long time. Kevenski —you met him yesterday—Kevenski and I and a couple of other guys started it." He chuckled, a deep-toned and somewhat startling noise which originated some place in the center of his barrel chest. "Lot of people think we were old Army buddies; truth is we met in the unemployment office." The company had clicked, thought not in a big way. For some years it had rolled along smoothly enough and then things had started to become hectic. "Came the Fifties," said Baxter—he made them sound like the Years of Doom on the soundtrack of a TV documentary—"came the Fifties and everything took off. No more staying even. You could go up or you could go under, but no more staying even. Diversify or die; diversify or die. I got that out of a business magazine," he added.

It reminded me of the description Epstein had once given me of his own business. It was like roaring downhill in a car with no brakes, clinging to the steering wheel and hoping you could make each corner. They had pushed events and been pushed by them; they were chasing the market place and trying to keep one jump ahead of it at the same time. They had started with one line and now they had three, plus a growing state of confusion.

"So you see," he finished, examining his coffee with an air of suspicion, "we're busting out of our girdle. I figure we've reached the point where we better have somebody in charge of each line.

We can't offer much—I'll be honest about that—and I won't make
any promises about the future because God only knows what's going to happen. Personally, I think it's going to be good. We've
handled everything that came along so far and we can handle
everything that's going to come, but that's my own opinion. Anyone walks in here can make up their own mind about that. For the
record, what we've got is a lot of work and no glory."

He stopped abruptly and stared at me.

"I just finished doing some work as a consultant," I said,
"and . . ."

"Yes, I know. Kevenski told me about it. Or he told me as much
as you told him; I gather it wasn't much."

"Well, the details aren't important anyway; the nature of the job
is. It was another business I didn't know anything about but that's
not the point. They hired me for what I *did* know. Advertising,
merchandising—oh, that's not the guts of the thing either. What I
did do was to pull a lot of stuff together in the right order and wrap
it up in a package which somebody could handle. And that's what
I've always done, when you come right down to it; that's what's behind every paragraph in that résumé."

Then I went on talking, because it was too late to turn back
now. I dug into my own résumé and I talked about every job I had
ever held and about the late nights and the sudden trips and the
problems which came at you from every angle and, above all, how
it was all sorted out and hammered into something which made
sense and could be used. This was what I could do; make something out of a lot of everything, and this is what I liked to do. Half-
way through this recital Baxter started nodding, as if he recognized
the things I was talking about, and when I had finished he said only,
"Fair enough. Let's get back to the shop."

We went back across the street and up to his office, where he sat
down behind his desk.

"Oh, by the way," he said. "I believe Kevenski told you the
salary that goes with the job. What was your reaction?"

It was a good salary, one we could get by on comfortably. I had
made a lot more, but I had done my damnedest to land jobs which
paid a lot less. It was a beginning and I told Baxter that it was
okay.

"Well, then," he said, tilting back his chair and looking at the ceiling again. "I guess that's that. Kevenski likes you and Donnell likes you and . ." he tilted forward again and looked straight at me across his desk ". . . I like you." That deep, rumbling chuckle sounded in his chest again. "You've got the only legitimate reason I know of for getting into this business—you like to live with chaos. Can you start Monday?"

"Yes," I said, "sure. Monday."

He stood up and pushed out his big hand and I shook it.

"I think we've both made a good choice," he said. "And I'm a pretty good guesser. Kevenski doesn't believe that, but it's true."

I took the train back to the city and as it pulled into the station I looked at my watch and thought dammit, it was too late to check Epstein's office for any messages. I'd be lucky if I made Grand Central in time. I wouldn't be going to the cubicle in Epstein's office any more but somehow that fact hadn't sunk in yet. This wasn't the way we'd planned it. I was supposed to rush to the phone and call Janet and she was supposed to hop the train into the city and we would then have the biggest and loudest and most uproarious celebration in living memory. But there wasn't time to phone Janet and I didn't have enough money with me for a celebration. I felt tired, anyway; terribly tired and confused and frightened. I was going to work with people again, not just step in from the outside for a few hours a day as I had done at Gilbrick's, but really work with them and be a part of their jobs and a part of their lives. I could handle the job—I'd handled the Gilbrick job—but the people, the office routine, the ordinary to and fro and the lunch table conversations and the company jokes . . . I had spent a long time in a distant land and now I was going to step into the normal world of ordinary, secure people again, just as if nothing had ever happened. I felt something which was like stage fright but was far deeper and much more terrifying.

And then the whole business became purely ridiculous because I fell asleep and for the first time in my life as a commuter I rode past my station. Janet went home—this was the procedure we'd agreed on if this ever happened—and I got off at the next stop up the line and telephoned her and, since it was only a few miles, she came and picked me up. I opened the car door and got behind the wheel and swung the car out of the station, stopping at the edge of the parking lot because the exit was a dangerous one. Then I

|189|

pulled onto the highway and stepped on the gas and I said, "You were right; this one came through. I got the job. It isn't the greatest, but it's good. It's better than I'd hoped for."

She didn't say anything.

"I got the job," I repeated, but she still didn't say anything so I looked at her, and as the car passed under a street light and the harsh, blue-white glare swept over her face, I saw she was crying.

EPILOGUE

Man
at a Desk

In one sense, at least, the tale of the job hunter ends here. There were other chapters, of course, but they came after Job Hunter, Inc. closed its doors and they belong to another story.

I sat down at my new desk at 9:30 that Monday morning and at 9:45 the phone rang and a crisp voice asked if they should framstabble the whatzit or just bangfrazzle the bonk and let it go at that? Whatever it meant, it was my baby; mine and nobody else's. "I'll be right down," I said.

The first few weeks were like that; awkward, bewildering, frightening. I fumbled my way through the regular office routine and felt oddly self-conscious, like an actor struggling with a part which didn't suit him. Two or three times I was sure I had blown the whole business and I sweated through agonizing weekends, expecting the ax to fall on Monday. With a little luck on my side and a lot of patience on theirs I blundered past those weeks, and then I began to get the feel of things. The faces around me became more familiar and I handled the problems which came up more skillfully because more and more of them were problems I had handled from the beginning. Everything settled down and everything was okay and everything was the same as it always had been—except that it wasn't.

I think this first hit me when X phoned. His name isn't important but he headed up the agency which had taken the Gilbrick account and he had a problem. The Gilbrick people had the bit in their teeth now; they had boosted their sales and upped their budget and the kid who was handling the account was a good kid but he was getting in over his head. They wanted somebody older—I smiled a bit grimly at that—somebody like the consultant who had helped straighten them out.

There it was, the road back. I thought of my old business and the years I had put into it and the people I knew and even the little things like the chatter around the water cooler and the perpetual smell of paste in the art department. I missed them so much that the memory was a physical pain, but I called X back and I told him "no."

Perhaps this was the wrong decision. I'll never really know. There was no bitterness in it, however, and no disillusion. There were some practical reasons, of course; I had latched on to a growing company and in Baxter's basso chuckle I sometimes heard the captain of that pirate brig which would cut down the fat merchantmen. Then there was the job itself. My title was smaller but my real authority was greater. There were few memos, fewer meetings; I ran my department and reported my results, good or bad, and I was the guy who was paid to stick his neck out. I could feel corners of my brain uncoiling and old ambitions and ideas slowly stirring again and I felt alive. I wasn't where I wanted to be, but I was doing what I wanted to do.

Beyond all this, however, some subtle sense told me that wherever I went—even to my old haunts—I'd be starting all over again. If I went back to where I had been, I would have to go back to what I had been, and I wasn't sure I could do it. The word "job" had a different meaning now and I no longer spelled "success" the same way; I had begun to measure it by the work I did and not by the badge I wore. No, there was no turning back. The old days had served their purpose and I looked back on them with a certain affection and with wry amusement, but there was no turning back. Things change and people change and you have to keep pushing ahead.

I don't necessarily think that I'm any "better" or that what some people like to refer to as my sense of values is any purer. They're just different and if they happen to be a little closer to reality I suppose that's a bonus, but it's hardly a virtue. There are some scars, in fact; they've not very pleasant ones and I can only hope that they're not permanent. Something seems to have happened to my ability to believe, for example. I like my job but I have no faith in its permanence or the permanence of any relationship between a man and an organization. No matter how well I do, no matter how close this relationship becomes, I still expect them to walk in one day and say "The water cooler's been fixed and those new sub-assemblies are on order and, oh, by the way, you're fired." Five years, ten years, fifteen years, it won't make any difference. It will all end that casually and I'll clean out my desk and go back to the phone booth in Grand Central. Common sense tells me this is foolish, but I still keep very little personal stuff in my desk. It could all be carried away in an attaché case.

There's something else, something ever uglier, which stands between me and my new colleagues. Baxter, Kevenski, Donnell, the girls in the office, the foremen on the shop floor, they're all fine people and they're all friends, but there's something about them I don't know, something I'll never know about any new friend. I don't know which one of them kicks the cat when nobody's looking.

Max summed it up well, I think. He came down from Connecticut, bearing a magnificent set of mellow old brass fixtures as a gift for our new home, and when I tried to talk about these troubles he simply nodded:

"It's simple enough; it's nothing new. Should I tell you?"

"Why, sure; of course."

"No, it's not something to say 'of course' about. You are both new at this and I don't want to scare you."

"For God's sake, Max," I said, "stop playing the patriarch and spill it."

"Very well. You have only one home, only one people, and if you lose them you never find others, not quite in the same way. There is a vast new race we created; the biggest contribution our century has made to history. And now you have joined it."

"Joined *what*, Max?"

|193|

The Job Hunter: The Diary
of a "Lost" Year

"The refugees. You are feeling just a little bit, I think, what they feel. Oh, you are luxury-class refugees, of course; no starvation, no crawling across borders, no waiting for visas, year after year after year, not yet, at least. But the confusion, the feeling of being apart —yes, that's typical. There are so many refugees in the world. Does it surprise you that some of them are American?"

The old friends, the trusted friends remained, though we see them less often. Margy and Mel come down about once a month. Mel thinks the house is "quaint"; he refers to my new job as "that thing you do" and asks occasionally when I'm going to get "a decent position." But Mel doesn't bother me any more because I've got him pegged. All that integrity and respectability, I know, are just a front; behind it Mel is really a nice guy. Perhaps he just never had any advantages.

Skip brightened up after we moved. He adopted the new home with enthusiasm and it occurred to me as I watched him gallop around the backyard that he had never really been happy in our former house. I don't know why. We waited for the new environment to work some similar change in Cliff, but it didn't. He seemed to feel in some vague way that the move had taken something from him and his air of resentment has deepened into a part of his personality. There isn't much we can do, apparently, but wait until he theoretically becomes an adult and moves into whatever world exists at that time.

Phil switched jobs. He picked his own moment, packed his battered briefcase and stepped easily from one office to another, leaving behind an indignant employer who had been picking *his* own moment to swing the ax. There's a knack to this and Phil has it. Plus luck, of course; it helps if you have that touch of luck.

Les writes from time to time—long, enthusiastic letters with a thread of nostalgia running through them. "Just once a year," he wrote recently, "I'd like to spend an hour strolling along Fifth Avenue. Then I could come back here and pitch in happily for another twelve months." He's planning a vacation in New York, but it won't be before next year because "we've got a lot of things going."

I go into the city two or three times a month and the other day, when I was cutting through Grand Central, I bumped into Sid and learned that there'd been a shake-up at his shop. Sid was out and he had been out for a couple of months and he was beginning to get a bit worried. He had several things on the fire, of course, and everyone was very encouraging, but somehow he just couldn't seem to make things *move*. There wasn't very much I could say. I could look into his future and, barring a lucky break, I could see the park bench and the personnel managers and the sore feet and the nights of panic. I couldn't very well tell him to cheer up, it wasn't as bad as he thought; not when I knew it was worse than he thought and worse than he could ever begin to imagine—yet. Later on, perhaps, he might reach that point where he felt there was something wrong with him personally and that he was all washed up and then I could tell him this wasn't so. I could buy him a lunch at Philippe's and give him some hints and let him know that other people had gone through it and that it wasn't just happening to him alone. Sid would make it okay, but he might have to walk down some long roads and search in some strange corners before he got there and it was still too early to talk to him about such things.

I gave him my phone number and urged him to keep in touch and then I stood by the phone booths for a moment and watched him walk away across the vast station floor: the job hunter, trudging toward the goal that was so many weary steps away.